Conflict
at
Work

The Companion Workbook

Dr. M. Paula Daoust

Conflict at Work: The Companion Workbook
Dr. M. Paula Daoust
Copyright © 2021 Maplewheat Publishing
Cover design: Germancreative
Editor: Frieda Paton
Assistant Editors: Dorissa Daoust and Pamela Brisendine
All Rights Reserved.

First Printing: February 2021
ISBN: 978-0-9778955-4-0
Dr. M. Paula Daoust
Behavior Transitions
10940 Parallel Pkwy, Suite K-182
Kansas City, KS 66109
(785) 633-6078
www.BehaviorTransitions.com
www.ConflictatWorkBook.com

Additional resource material for this workbook is available at: www.conflictatworkbook.com/resources/

Do you have a group that would benefit from better conflict management skills? Dr. Daoust is available for keynote presentations or workshops tailored specifically to your needs.

Contact Dr. Daoust at:

Dr.Paula@behaviortransitions.com
785-633-6078

Additional resource material for this workbook, including worksheets and self-hypnosis recordings, is available at:

www.conflictatworkbook.com/resources

Conflict at Work
The Companion Workbook

Written by a leading expert in performance management with over 40 years of experience

Dr. M. Paula Daoust has a doctorate in Behavior Psychology and is an expert in helping people find and maintain their peak performance. She is also a certified hypnotherapist and seamlessly blends these tools into her coaching to help people easily achieve lasting change. Over a period of 25 years, she has taught hundreds of master-level students how to be more persuasive and influential, and how to successfully manage conflict.

Dr. M. Paula Daoust is the expert other leaders look to for help in finding their peak performance. She has taught workshops and spoken at events all over North America on subjects such as conflict, change management, storytelling, influence and power, anxiety and stress at work and peak performance.

Table of Contents

One
Overview

Why this book?

Conflict doesn't have to be a bad thing. When conflict is handled well, it can guide you to the results you need and want, and it can contribute to a stronger relationship. If you are like most people, however, this has not been your experience. It is more likely that conflict has frequently caused you emotional pain and frustration. Most of the strategies for managing conflict that we learned while growing up - from our parents, friends, and the media - are not very effective at best and, at worst, they can be counter-productive and outright destructive. The price for this is failed relationships, derailed careers, poorer productivity, quality, and efficiency, and toxic work environments.

> *Most of the strategies for managing conflict that we learned while growing up - from our parents, friends and the media - are not very effective at best and, at worst, they can be counter-productive and outright destructive.*

Imagine the difference it would make to your career if you were good at resolving conflict! How would that differentiate you from 90% of your colleagues? How much easier would it be to get things done at work? How much more fun would it be to go to work, knowing that your team supported one another and worked well with other teams? If dysfunctional conflict were eliminated from your work environment, what effect would this have on your creative problem-solving? The benefits to you and your organization would be dramatic!

The book, *Conflict at Work*, provides many tools and also some guidance on which tools are best suited for each situation. While studying this book is a giant step toward becoming a master of conflict resolution, it isn't enough. Just because you invest in an expensive bicycle doesn't mean you automatically become an elite cyclist. It's the same for conflict management. The book is a beginning but if you want to improve your conflict management skills, you will have to invest some time and effort into training.

That's what this workbook provides for you. It outlines specific exercises to better understand each of the skills described in *Conflict at Work*. Complete the exercises and take the time to journal, and you will get results.

> *The better you get at managing conflict, the less conflict you will encounter!*

It's interesting that the better you get at managing conflict, the less conflict you will encounter! It isn't that the potential for conflict disappears. You just become better at dealing with conflict in the early stages. The sooner you address a conflict effectively, the less effort it takes. You might not even recognize it as a conflict because you calmly stepped up and applied the right tool at the right time.

How to use this book

This workbook was designed to stand on its own, but it is much better when paired with its sister, *Conflict at Work*. Every chapter in the workbook has an overview of the concepts, but a much more detailed description of the concept and its importance is provided in *Conflict at Work*. Taking the time to read the matching chapter in the sister book will help you get more out of the exercises and journal questions.

Each chapter in this workbook follows the same pattern: an overview of the essential concepts, some exercises to practice applying the skills and concepts, and some questions designed to prompt greater insight and self-awareness. These questions will challenge your thinking on a deeper level, and tap into your subconscious knowledge and wisdom.

Each chapter is independent of the other chapters so there is no need to work through the chapters in sequence. Feel free to move around and work on those skills which you feel you need to develop or those you feel most comfortable using.

A word about journaling

I strongly encourage you to take advantage of the journaling questions that appear at the end of each chapter. Our brains process thoughts at lightning speed. This means that you don't always make the connections between the various thoughts in your mind and your situation. Sometimes an answer to a problem or an effective strategy for resolving a conflict is right there in front of you but you just aren't seeing it.

When you journal, you improve the probability of seeing the whole picture. That's because we write so much slower than we think. It is estimated that we process 600-700 words per minute. Compare this with the average writing speed of about 15-20 words per minute. Writing forces you to slow down your thinking and this allows for deeper processing of ideas and feelings.

While you journal, you could notice some ties between your feelings and your behavior that might otherwise slip past your awareness. Journaling will provide you with interesting insights about yourself and your patterns of behavior. It also serves as a mindfulness exercise. It helps you to clear your mind by getting thoughts down on paper and this can be a valuable avenue for stress-relief. Do yourself a favor and don't skip past the journal questions. Furthermore, although you are asked to choose one of several questions as your focus for a journal exercise, you don't have to limit yourself to just one journaling session per chapter.

The tools

The tools in this book are organized in sections. Chapters 1–3 will provide you with an overview of conflict management and guide you in re-thinking some of the things you learned about conflict while growing up. These chapters will help you to recognize how you have been getting in your own way and will introduce you to more effective ways of thinking about conflict.

Chapters 4 and 5 focus on managing your emotions when entering a difficult conversation. Understanding how your physiology influences your behavior and how to take back control is a major step toward a better resolution in difficult situations. Learning to create a positive mindset and to appreciate your strengths will reduce the stress response and guide you to your best thinking, even under pressure.

Chapters 6 through to 11 describe powerful tools for action. To be effective, the tool needs to be a good match for the demands of the situation and you need to be comfortable with using it. The range of tools described in these chapters, combined with the practice exercises, will make this possible for you to select and use the right tool for any situation.

The tools in these chapters include kindness, using language more effectively, applying behavioral science to condition healthier responses, understanding how self-hypnosis can neutralize tension, using the paradoxical Aiki tool for getting unstuck and finally the CLEAN/N model for holding the difficult conversation.

Chapter 12 delivers a strategy for identifying which tools to consider for which situations. Since we don't always know when we are about to encounter a conflict, Chapter 13 offers you some guidance for times when you are blindsided and have to respond in the moment. Finally, Chapter 14 wraps all this up and challenges you to step up to conflict with calmly and with courage.

What to expect

I have some bad news for you. However, it's really not news at all because I am confident that you already know this. Just reading this book will not magically equip you with everything you need to make conflict in your life disappear. It

> *As long as there are two or more people involved in any endeavor, there will be some level of conflict.*
>
> *But you don't have to be afraid of it!*

will take time and practice to become better at managing conflict and, no matter how good you get at managing conflict, it will always remain a part of your life. As long as there are two or more people involved in any endeavor, there will be some level of conflict. But you don't have to be afraid of it! You can practice using the tools in this book and learn to use conflict as a healthy, opportunity for growth instead of a dysfunctional and dispiriting experience.

Just as these tools won't make conflict disappear from your life, they will also not necessarily make the management of conflict easy. But they will help you to get the results you need and want while strengthening important relationships. I promise you, the time and effort you put into becoming more effective at managing conflict will have a positive impact on your career, your relationships, and your quality of life. You deserve the good things in life and they will be there for the taking when you improve your conflict management skills.

That's what this workbook provides for you. It outlines specific exercises to better understand each of the skills described in *Conflict at Work*. Complete the exercises and take the time to journal, and you will get results.

It's interesting that the better you get at managing conflict, the less conflict you will encounter! It isn't that the potential for conflict disappears, it's just that you are better at dealing with it early in its development. The earlier you effectively address a conflict, the less effort it takes. You might not even recognize it as a conflict because you calmly stepped up and applied the right tool at the right time.

Conflict is emotional.

You can't "think" your way out of a conflict.

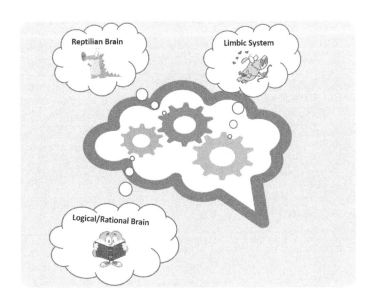

Two
Whole Brain Conflict Management

Using your whole brain

It's one thing to learn the steps necessary for good conflict management, but it's a whole other thing to put those steps into action. Learning is a cognitive function and involves the executive function of our brain, which is located in the prefrontal cortex (PFC). The PFC is the logical, rational, thinking part of our brain.

But conflict is not a cognitive event - it is an emotional experience. At the root of all conflict is a sense of threat which evokes fear. The source of all emotions is the limbic system and the reptilian brain which operate at the subconscious level.

When you detect an impending conflict, your emotional brain goes into high alert and activates your survival response of fight-or-flight. Your body is flooded with cortisol and adrenaline and the surge in production of these neurotransmitters deteriorates your thinking. Faced with this all-consuming emotional reaction, your response will be at its worst when you need it to be at its best.

You need to use your whole brain to manage conflict effectively - both your rational, logical brain and your emotional brain. You need strategies that will help you to refocus your emotions so that you can feel confident, courageous, and calm instead of defensive and stressed. You also want to be able to think clearly so that you can respond to situations in a way that the conflict can either be averted or managed constructively. When you can do this, conflict can improve the quality of life, not damage it. A well-managed conflict can lead to excellent results for both parties and strengthen relationships.

Getting your baseline

To begin this journey toward mastering the conflict management challenge, it would be helpful to get a baseline measurement of your current response to conflict. As you work through the exercises in this workbook and apply what you learn, you can retake this brief assessment and watch your score improve.

Disaster to Master:
How good are you at managing conflict?

		Rarely / Never	Seldom	Sometimes	Often	Almost Always
1.	If someone disagrees with me, I vigorously defend the issue.					
2.	Even if I don't agree, I go along with suggestions from co-workers.					
3.	I have difficulty thinking clearly when dealing with a difficult conversation.					
4.	In a conflict, I get what I want even if it damages the relationship.					
5.	In a conflict, my emotions take over and I say and do things I didn't intend to say or do.					
6.	When a conflict does not go well, I find it hard to ask for a "do-over."					
7.	I just leave the room when I find myself in a conflict.					
8.	When in a problem situation, I avoid the give-and-take of negotiation.					
9.	When in a conflict, I raise my voice and try to dominate the discussion.					
10.	When in a conflict, I say hurtful things I don't mean or call the other party names.					
11.	I recruit co-workers as allies to take my side and help me to deal with a conflict.					
12.	The natural outcome of a conflict is a damaged relationship with the other party.					
13.	When I am in a disagreement, I have all the information I need.					
14.	When in a conflict, I try to say very little and leave as soon as I can.					
15.	Being in disagreement with others makes me feel uncomfortable and anxious.					

		Rarely / Never	Seldom	Sometimes	Often	Almost Always
16.	When in a conflict, it is not possible to find solutions that will satisfy everyone.					
17.	I may not get what I want but it is a small price to pay for keeping the peace.					
18	In a conflict, I argue my case and insist on the advantages of my point.					
19.	In a conflict, my focus is on winning.					
20	I avoid differences of opinion as much as possible.					
	Column Total (*Add up the number of checks in a column and multiply.*)	# X 4 = ___	# X 3 = ___	# X 2 = ___	# X 1 = ___	# X 0 = ___
	Grand Total					

How good are you at managing conflict?

Master	—	61 - 80
Effective	—	46 - 60
Challenged	—	31 - 45
Problematic	—	16 - 30
Disaster	—	0 - 15

Deeper Thoughts

Set a timer for five minutes. Choose one of the following questions and write down your answer. Continue writing until the timer rings.

1. What has contributed to my score on this assessment? What lessons did I learn while growing up that taught me to respond to conflict the way I do?
2. Did the score on my assessment surprise me? Why or why not?
3. When I anticipate a conflict, what thoughts are going through my head? What am I feeling? Why?
4. What is it about conflict that I find most uncomfortable? Am I worried that others are taking advantage of me or do I worry about damaging an important relationship? Or is it both?
5. In the past, what advice about managing conflict have I been given? Has it been helpful? If so, how was it helpful? If not, why not?

My thoughts:

Different levels of conflict require different approaches.

Three
Levels of Conflict

What is conflict?

Conflict is defined as "a competitive or opposing action of incompatibles. It is an antagonistic state of action - as of divergent ideas, interests, or persons." We tend to use the term "conflict" rather loosely to describe any challenge we encounter but many of these challenges do not meet the definition of a true conflict.

The continuum of conflict

There is a continuum of challenges. If a situation at the lower levels of the continuum is not dealt with properly, it will escalate to the level of a full-blown, destructive conflict. You already understand this intuitively and, because you know these lower levels on the conflict continuum can become a dispute or discord, we tend to respond to them in the same way as to conflicts at the higher end of the continuum. This is a mistake because our discomfort with, or fear of, the higher-level conflicts gets in the way of effectively addressing the lower-level challenges.

Ignoring a problem rarely makes it go away. It is a paradox that our discomfort or outright fear of conflict is the very mechanism that allows a challenge to rise through the continuum to become the onflict we are trying to avoid. The

> *"A stitch in time saves nine."*
> *It is much easier to resolve a conflict earlier rather than later.*

tools for effectively addressing lower-level challenges take less time or energy to implement and involve far less stress than the tools needed to resolve a conflict at the higher end of the continuum.

When you identify what level on the continuum of conflict a challenge is sitting, you can use the right tools and prevent a full-blown conflict from emerging. The adage, "A stitch in time saves nine," applies here. It is much easier to resolve a conflict earlier rather than later. For this reason, it is helpful to understand the continuum and to identify on which level your challenge rests.

Levels in the Continuum of Conflict

Level 1 – Irritation.

> You feel annoyed or irritated about something.

Level 2 – Worried or troubled.

> You don't feel safe and anxiety about what will happen next is growing.

Level 3 – Misunderstanding.

> There is a breakdown in communication and you or the other party has misread signals: words or gestures.

Level 4 – Disagreement.

> You and the other party have a difference of opinion on appropriate action.

Level 5 – Argument.

> You are in opposition to another party and you have a strongly-held and coherent set of reasons, statements, or facts to support your position.

Level 6 – Dispute.

> The disagreement or argument has escalated to include anger or frustration. Winning is now the focus, not understanding. You are feeling some sense of righteousness which is fueling your determination to achieve your chosen outcome.

Level 7 - Discord.

> You are fully engaged in a zero-sum game. Your own and the other party's perspectives are mutually exclusive.

Why conflict is so hard to resolve

Regardless of where the event lies on the continuum of conflict, something of value is being threatened. This sense of threat is why resolving any level of conflict becomes such a challenge. It doesn't matter whether the threat is real or perceived - any threat produces fear. Fear belongs to the emotional brain, but most conflict models attempt to resolve the conflict as a rational, logical event. These models do little to ease the fear or to build courage.

> *Estimates are that only 5% of our decisions are made by the rational brain.*

Relying on the rational, logical brain to do the hard work of conflict management is a fool's errand because the emotional brain is far more powerful in influencing our behavior than the rational brain. Estimates are that only 5% of our decisions are made by the rational brain. Resolving conflict at any level requires a comprehensive approach that goes beyond cognitive, rational tools and integrates what science tells us about the brain and behavior.

Use the right tool for the situation

Using the wrong conflict management tools at any level of the continuum is a prescription for trouble. Unresolved conflict disrupts and even destroys careers. It damages organizations because of poor decisions and higher than necessary turnover. When you know where the challenge sits on the continuum of conflict, you can match the right combination of tools to ease negative emotions and create the right space for effective problem-solving.

Exercises

1. For each of the following scenarios, decide which level on the conflict continuum it represents and explain why you think so.
   (*Check your answers on page 154.*)

> ### Levels of the Continuum of Conflict
>
> 1-Irritation; 2-Worried or Troubled; 3-Misunderstanding;
> 4-Disagreement; 5-Argument; 6-Dispute; 7-Discord

   a. Your data is not reliable and I just can't agree to that strategy. My data indicates that we need to take this slower.

   Level: _____

   b. I didn't want to come to this meeting. I have ten urgent emails I should be responding to and instead, I'm sitting in this conference room waiting for George to get here so we can get started.

   Level: _____

   c. I have done this a hundred times and I know what works. I am not about to settle for anything less because I know I'm right. Get on board or get out of my way.

   Level: _____

   d. After I worked overtime to get the report done on time, Raoul was really critical of some of my conclusions. Now I'm not sure if I can work with Raoul. I'm just not sure of exactly what he wants.

   Level: _____

   e. If we do it your way, we are going to polarize the team.

   Level: _____

f. I sent a detailed email explaining my problem and asking for Brad's input. His response missed the point of my question. I don't think he gets what I'm trying to do and I wonder if he just doesn't want to be bothered.

Level: _____

g. I'm not going to stand for this. This is just not how we do business.

Level: _____

2. For each of the levels of the conflict continuum, provide an example from your life.

Level	Personal Example
Level 1: Irritation	
Level 2: Worried/Troubled	
Level 3: Misunderstanding	
Level 4: Disagreement	
Level 5: Argument	
Level 6: Dispute	
Level 7: Discord	

3. Identify five different conflicts that you have dealt with in the last four weeks. Sometimes it is easier to remember them if you review your calendar for this period. Give each conflict a name, identify the highest level on the continuum that it reached, and explain why you to assigned this level.

Conflict	Level	Rationale for choice of level	

What do the levels of these five conflicts tell you about your pattern of conflict? Are you comfortable with your observation? If so, why? If not, why not?

_____

_____

_____

_____

_____

_____

_____

_____

4. Not handling a conflict can derail a career but people who are good at resolving a conflict flourish.

   a. Identify someone you have observed who is not good at managing conflict. What do they do when they are confronted with conflict? Describe the impact it had or is having on this person's career.

Response to conflict	Impact on their career

   b. Identify someone you have observed who has managed conflicts well. Describe what they do differently than your previous example and what impact it has had on their career.

Response to conflict	Impact on their career

Deeper Thoughts

Set a timer for five minutes. Choose one of the following questions and write down your answer. Continue writing until the timer rings.

1. For which of the seven levels was it the hardest to find an example? Which was the easiest? What does this tell me?
2. For a conflict that rose to level 5 or above, describe the path it took through the various levels.
3. What pattern can I detect in the conflicts I am encountering? Are they all over the continuum or do they tend to represent one or two levels? What does the pattern or lack of pattern tell me?
4. When I encounter a conflict, what is my go-to response? How effective is it? Does it change as the conflict rises through the continuum?
5. What impact has conflict had on my career? What would change if I improved my conflict resolution skills?

My thoughts:

_____

_____

_____

_____

_____

_____

_____

_____

_____

_____

_____

_____

_____

_____

The meaning we attach to our facts determines our behavior and then our outcome.

Facts	→	Story

$$A + B + C = D \text{ or } E \text{ or maybe } R ?$$

Four
Common Approaches to Conflict

Which club is yours?

In the absence of training, people tend to respond to conflict by joining one of two clubs and sometimes, they bounce between both clubs - the Valiant Warrior Club and the White Knight Club.

Members of the Valiant Warrior club see the conflict as a battlefield. Winning is essential and losing is unacceptable. They see themselves as having been wronged by the other party and they seek to right that wrong and come out victorious.

> *Members of the Valiant Warrior Club see conflict as a battlefield. Winning is essential and losing is unacceptable.*

> *Members of the White Knight Club see themselves as victims to be rescued from their situation.*

The White Knight club is at the other extreme. Like members of the Valiant Warrior Club, they see themselves as victims but, rather than righting a wrong themselves, they expect that someone should rescue them from their situation. They avoid dealing with the conflict directly and instead seek others to step in and fight their battle. They paint themselves as helpless and innocent and appeal to the sense of justice of others who are more powerful.

Regardless of which club you belong to, the result is the same. The battle is never really won. Members of the White Knight club are never rescued and their distress and misery will continue. In the short term, members of the Valiant Warrior club might feel that they have won a battle, but it is always at the cost of damaging important relationships. In relationships, when one person loses, no one can win. The loser will eventually exact a price for the loss and so the battle continues.

To which club do you belong? Or, when confronted with a conflict, do you start in one club and switch mid-stream? There are those who hope that the conflict will go away if they can wait it out, or they tell themselves that they will take the high road and let it go, they won't let it bother them. Then they join the Valiant Warrior club when something happens and they can't take it anymore. Others will respond to a conflict by immediately going to war and then, when they begin to see the consequences of doing battle, shift to the White Knight club and appeal to others for rescue. Bouncing between clubs is not the answer but neither is membership to either club a healthy option. You deserve better than either club can offer you!

Meaning-makers

You don't have to choose between either club. There is another way to deal with conflict, but first you need to think about conflict differently.

Thinking differently begins with understanding how our brains are wired to attach meaning to events. One of the many ways that differentiates humans from all other species is that we are meaning-makers. When a sequence of events happens, we scan our warehouse of stored patterns and attach a meaning to the event – we look for an explanation. The meaning we attach is our own conclusion as to why something happened, or it is a judgment of whether the event is good/bad, or safe/threatening. "She threw her gloves down because she was frustrated with the situation," or, "He tossed his little daughter in the air and told her she was a good girl because she just used the potty," or, "He isn't eating his broccoli because he hates it."

When anything happens, we make a judgment or draw a conclusion in a split-second, and we are usually unaware that we have done so. The meaning or judgment we attached to an event is woven so tightly with the actual event that, in our minds, they become one. This action of attaching meaning and judgment to events is hard-wired for a good reason. It helps us make sense of our world and identify when something might either harm us or help us. It provides us with some predictability in an otherwise confusing world and allows us to feel some sense of control.

> *The meaning or judgment we attach to an event determines how we will respond.*

The meaning or judgment we attach to an event determines how we will respond it. If your supervisor stops by your desk and asks for the report you have been working on, there are several potential meanings you could attach to this event. You might think, "She doesn't understand how challenging this report is and she is being unfair to ask for it right now," or, "She is being pressured by her boss and really needs me to come through for her."

If the meaning you attached is the former, you will feel defensive or disrespected and you might respond with impatience or resistance. Alternatively, if your meaning was the latter, you might feel some empathy for your supervisor and work even harder to get the report out in a timely manner.

In the above scenario, there are many other meanings that could be attached to the same set of events or facts. The meaning you attach to your supervisor's request is influenced by your past experience and your own internal sense of competence and current stress level.

The sad reality is that, in addition to being wired to attach meaning, you will attach a negative judgment to the sequence of facts unless there is clear evidence that the situation is a good thing or at least not a personal threat. In other words, you are wired

> *Unless your experience tells you that a situation is safe, you will assume there is a threat.*

for the dark side. This makes sense because if you assume something will do you harm, you can take proactive steps to protect yourself. You are less vulnerable to harm when you judge a sequence of events as a threat.

When our ancestors encountered a lion, tiger, or bear, survival depended on judging the situation as a threat. In our complex society, you are not likely to encounter a lion, tiger, or bear outside of the zoo, but your brain's hard-wiring has not changed very much. Your reptilian brain triggers alarms when a car cuts you off in traffic, when colleagues stop talking after you enter the break room, or when you are asked a difficult question in a meeting. Unless your experience tells you that a situation is safe, you will assume there is a threat.

Facts vs. meaning

This predilection to attach a negative meaning to an event is the source of many conflicts. The speed at which this happens tricks us into confusing the meaning with the facts. A first step in resolving conflict is to unravel the facts from the meaning we have attached to an event. A fact can be captured on a video camera. It can be seen and/or heard. A fact is objective, it can be verified.

Meaning is something that happens in your head. It is a conclusion or a judgment. Adjectives and adverbs are descriptors and, as such, are part of the meaning or judgment you have applied to a set of facts. Two people can see or hear exactly the same thing but come away with different meanings.

Janie smiled after you told her she did a good job. What conclusion or judgment do you draw from the smile? Did she smile because she was proud of her work or was she simply relieved that you didn't criticize the work? Your words of praise and Janie's smile are verifiable facts but there are multiple meanings that can be attached to the same set of facts.

Recognizing that your meaning is not a fact and that there are other meanings that could be attached to the same set of facts is a key to resolving conflict. Just recognizing that the other party might have a different perspective on what just happened can slow your response. Taking time to consider another perspective might help you to avoid putting your foot in your mouth!

> *For any set of facts, there can be many different meanings. When you recognize this, you can be more open to hearing the other person's meaning.*

For you, the meaning you attached to facts is your truth about what just happened. Often, your truth is the correct truth. Separating facts from your meaning doesn't require that you reject your meaning. You just need to be aware that there is more than one possible interpretation of the facts. When you do this, you open yourself to hearing the other party's perspective. It allows you to approach the situation with some curiosity and with that, to gather more information. Instead of attacking or rejecting the other person, you will listen. This reduces the sense of threat for both you and the other party and heightens the possibility of coming to a good result for both parties.

Exercises

1. Identifying facts.

    List the facts for each of the following scenarios. Be careful to list only things that could be verified.
    (*Check your answers on page 155.*)

    Example:

    The Rainyer project was a big, complicated assignment. It used to be Laurie's responsibility and, until she was promoted, she used to complain about it often. Now, it was Nate's problem. He was just about to head over to Laurie's office to get some advice on the next steps. He had the Rainyer folder and a list of questions in his padfolio. Just as he was leaving, he got a call from Laurie's administrative assistant asking to reschedule the meeting. Laurie's son had a fever and the school needed Laurie to pick him up. This was the second time Laurie had cancelled the meeting to discuss the project. Reluctantly, Nate put the Rainyer folder away and decided he would delay working on the project until he could meet with Laurie.

    Facts:

    - *The Rainyer project used to be Laurie's responsibility.*
    - *Laurie used to complain about the project.*
    - *Nate was bringing the Rainyer folder with a list of questions to the meeting with Laurie.*
    - *The meeting was cancelled.*
    - *This was the second cancellation.*
    - *Laurie had gotten a call from her son's school saying he had a fever.*
    - *Nate put the Rainyer folder away.*

    a. "Where is that report? I needed it an hour ago," Cal demanded.
        "I'm working on it, but the information Jill gave me doesn't balance. I need to check it out before I can finalize the report," Bob responded.

        Facts:

        _____

        _____

_____

_____

_____

b. "We can get started as soon as everyone is here. Anyone know where Mandy is?" Angela asked.

"Mandy is on Mandy-time. She's always 10 minutes late. We can start without her, she'll be here soon," Richard answered.

"No, this is too important. We need everyone's input. You can grab a cup of coffee while we wait," Angela insisted.

Facts:

_____

_____

_____

_____

_____

c. When Hayden got back to his desk, he found a note, "I thought we were meeting at 10. I'll check back with you later, Kate."

Hayden felt badly that he had missed Kate and immediately checked his calendar. He didn't see a meeting with Kate that he might have missed. He wondered what happened but remembered that this was not the first time Kate got her meeting schedule confused. He shrugged it off and began working on his latest project.

Facts:

_____

_____

_____

_____

_____

d. "The Chicago project has run into some snags. I need you to go out there tomorrow and see if you can fix it," Lance said.

Hannah wasn't happy with this news. She had promised to be at her daughter's recital the following night and traveling to Chicago would put that in jeopardy. Besides, Lance knew more about this project - he should be the one to go, not her. It wasn't fair that Lance was pushing this off on her!

Facts:

_____

_____

_____

_____

_____

e.   The sign above the microwave clearly stated, "No popcorn." That didn't seem to matter to Diane, as she munched on popcorn during the meeting.

Facts:

_____

_____

_____

_____

_____

2.   Seeing multiple meanings.
     For each of the scenarios in the previous exercise, provide at least three different meanings. At least one of the meanings should suggest a positive intention from the other party.
     (*Check your answers on page 157.*)

     Example:
     1.   *Laurie doesn't really want to help me with this project and is using her son to avoid the meeting.*
     2.   *Laurie knows I'm struggling with the Rainyer project but it isn't a priority for her.*
     3.   *Laurie's schedule is tight and she is trying to meet with me. She wants to help but things keep getting in the way.*

     a.   The report:
          Meanings:
          1. _____
          2. _____
          3. _____

b. The meeting:

Meanings:

1. _____

2. _____

3. _____

c. The note:

Meanings:

1. _____

2. _____

3. _____

d. Chicago:

Meanings:

1. _____

2. _____

3. _____

e. Popcorn:

Meanings:

1. _____

2. _____

3. _____

3. Unraveling your own facts from your meanings.

a. Consider a conflict in your past or that you are dealing with now. Set a timer for five minutes and describe in detail the context, the players, and what happened.

_____

_____

_____

_____

_____

_____

_____
_____
_____
_____
_____
_____

b. Review your description and list the facts. Check each fact you listed to make sure that if a video camera were available, it would be captured by the camera. Adjectives and adverbs usually indicate a judgment, not a fact.

_____
_____
_____
_____
_____
_____
_____
_____

c. Write three different meanings that fit your facts. At least one of your meanings should suggest a positive intent from the other party.

Meanings:

1. _____

2. _____

3. _____

Deeper Thoughts

Set a timer for five minutes. Choose one of the following questions and write down your answer. Continue writing until the timer rings.

1. Given the personal conflict described above, how did I feel when I drew each of the three meanings I identified? Did I feel less defensive or more empathy for the other party when I considered their perspective?

2. Consider another conflict you have dealt with in the past. Pretend you are the other party in the conflict. Describe the conflict in detail from that party's perspective, including the context and what happened. Does writing from their perspective change how you feel about the conflict?

3. Considering another party's perspective, or the meaning they might draw from the same set of facts, does not mean that you must accept their meaning. Explain to yourself why it is important to at least consider other meanings which could be drawn from the same set of facts.

4. Describe a situation in which you drew a conclusion and acted on it, just to discover more information later which proved that your conclusion was wrong. How did it feel? What damage was done to the outcome because you did not have all the facts and drew the wrong meaning?

5. When dealing with a conflict, why is it important to slow down and challenge the first meaning you draw? How will you do that?

My thoughts:

You have three brains, not one! Use them all.

Five
Conflict and Your Body

Survival instinct

Our most basic instinct is survival. When we are confronted with a challenge, in the absence of clear information otherwise, our minds will go to the dark side and assume that the challenge is a threat. Someone objects to an idea you have or responds to something you have said in an unexpected way and you will instinctively assess whether the challenge is a threat or not. If the situation is ambiguous, your bias is toward seeing it as threat.

Another implication of this survival instinct is that you are wired to avoid loss. You will defend and protect what you see as yours. Similarly, if you are prevented access to something that you value, you will see this as a threat. Behavioral economics research has demonstrated that

> *Loss avoidance means that you will put more energy toward avoiding a loss than to acquiring a similar gain.*

we will put more energy toward avoiding a loss than to acquiring a similar gain.

This makes compromising difficult when faced with a conflict because we overvalue our own possessions and undervalue those of others. We will experience a compromise as a loss and our wiring motivates us to avoid loss.

Triune brain

The way in which we respond to conflict is heavily influenced by the way our brain is wired. As stated previously, conflict is an emotional event and in order to respond effectively to conflict we need to understand more about how our brain deals with emotions. We don't have just one brain. We have three brains: reptilian, limbic, and prefrontal cortex (PFC). Each of our three brains has a role to play in helping us to survive and they interact with one another below our conscious awareness.

Reptilian brain

The primary function of the reptilian brain is self-preservation. It acts instinctively to protect the body. A major function of the reptilian brain is to constantly survey incoming stimuli and then to alert the other parts of the brain to any potential danger. You might think of it as our early warning system.

When dealing with conflict, an important aspect of the reptilian brain is the Reticular Activating System (RAS). A function of the RAS is to filter non-essential stimuli. This protects us from being distracted by every small change in our environment or from being overwhelmed by too many simultaneous stimuli. Ordinarily this is a good thing, but it does have a downside. The problem is that we are unaware of what is being filtered by the RAS and this limits our full perception of events.

> *We are unaware of what is being filtered by the RAS and this limits our full perception of events.*

You can attend a meeting and think you have seen and heard the same thing as your colleague sitting beside you. Most often you will discover this is not the case. Based on your history, values, and priorities, your RAS is filtering different information than your neighbor's RAS.

This filtering is often at the root of many conflicts and it can be a major stumbling block to conflict resolution. Your perception of a tense situation is almost guaranteed to be different from that of the other party. Your brain attended to and ignored different details than the other party's brain. It could be argued that, because of the RAS, two people will usually not be sharing the same reality.

The limbic system

The limbic system is the emotional brain. It is the storehouse of memories, habits, heuristics and the source of preferences and feelings. It uses images, not words, to process information and these images influence your behavior. When you anticipate a conflict and feel the dread welling up in your chest, you are creating a vivid picture of an unpleasant outcome. This vivid picture provides the map for your subconscious. It then begins acting in ways to realize the unpleasant outcome. This is the self-fulfilling prophecy in action.

Much of your behavior is controlled by habits. They help you to navigate your day-to-day decisions, big and small, with a minimal investment of energy. Habits are formed through repetition because, according to Hebb's Law, "When neurons fire together they wire together." This means that when a sequence of behavior is repeated often enough, the behaviors become knitted together and form a habit. The more often the sequence is fired, the stronger the habit.

Once a habit is formed, your response to a specific stimulus will be automatic. If, in the past, your pattern of response to a raised voice was to physically leave the environment, without thinking, this is what you will do the next time you encounter a raised voice. You can overcome this automatic response but it takes a deliberate effort and a lot of energy to do so. You are wired to take the path of least resistance, to act in ways that conserve energy. Unless there is a very good reason to act contrary to your habit, you probably won't invest that energy.

The amygdala and the hippocampus are two sub-systems of the limbic system that have a particular relevance to conflict. When the reptilian brain detects threat, it is the amygdala that reacts and sets off the fight-or-flight response. Your body is flooded with adrenaline and cortisol to prepare you for action.

All energy is directed to your internal organs and muscles, leaving only enough energy in the brain to maintain essential functions such as breathing and keeping your heart beating. When faced with a conflict, the consequence for thinking is that you are functioning on autopilot with little energy left for clear problem-solving. In essence, when the fight-or-flight response is in force, you are literally dumbed-down. Your rational brain is not firing on all cylinders because the energy to do so is not available.

> *When the fight-or-flight response is in force, you are literally dumbed-down.*

The fight-or-flight response has an additional consequence for your effective response to conflict. When your body is flooded with cortisol, the hippocampus can become overwhelmed and critical neurons are killed off faster than the body can reproduce them. The hippocampus is responsible for processing stimuli to create new learning and also for turning off the stress response. When it becomes overwhelmed, both of these functions are compromised. Your ability to learn from the conflict experience is weakened and, worse, it becomes difficult for you to "calm down." Neither of these outcomes will be helpful in negotiating a positive resolution to the conflict.

The limbic system and the reptilian brain combine to form the subconscious brain. We like to think we make rational, logical decisions and sometimes we do. However, depending on which expert you consult, it is argued that 90–95% of our decisions are made by the subconscious brain. The subconscious and conscious brains have been compared to a man riding an elephant. The man, the conscious brain, might think that he is in control. He does have some influence - but only as long as the elephant is willing to be directed. Once the elephant, the subconscious brain, has been excited, it takes over and the man can only hold on.

The prefrontal cortex

The prefrontal cortex (PFC) is the newest part of the brain to evolve and it is responsible for logical, rational decision-making -this is your conscious brain. This constant stream of thoughts entertaining you all day is a function of the PFC. The PFC is the rider and is heavily influenced by the elephant but, most importantly, it is usually unaware of the extent of this influence.

A plate of your favorite cookies, fresh from the oven, is sitting on the kitchen counter. Chances are you will forget all about your decision to eat fewer calories and will pop that gooey wonderfulness in your mouth. Your elephant was engaged and now your rider will obligingly provide you with a rationale: "I was hungry," or "I ate healthy all day, one cookie won't hurt," or "I exercised today, I deserve a little treat," or my personal favorite, "Pat worked hard to make these cookies. I can't hurt her/his feelings!"

The elephant, the subconscious brain, makes decisions faster than the rider, the conscious brain. The decision to eat the cookie comes before the rationale but you think it's the reverse. If there is a conflict between what the elephant wants and what the rider wants, the elephant will win. The rider will then provide a rational explanation for the elephant's decision and continue the illusion that it is in charge.

When the stress response, fight-or-flight, is in force, the PFC's ability to think deteriorates for two reasons. First, much of the oxygen required for processing complex data has been diverted to the internal organs and extremities in preparation for battle or escape. Second, as discussed earlier, the hippocampus is not functioning at full capacity. The cortisol that is raging in your body is slowing down or interrupting your ability to problem-solve effectively and you are responding on auto-pilot instead.

One way to reverse, or at least minimize, the effect of cortisol in your body is to engage in behaviors that trigger the production of the "happy" neurotransmitters. Neurotransmitters heavily influence our feelings and, as a result, our thinking. There are many neurotransmitters that contribute to a more positive mood, but the most famous are dopamine, oxytocin, serotonin, and endorphins (DOSE).

Triggering an increase of DOSE

Dopamine is the "more-ish" chemical. It activates the reward center of the brain and we always want more of it. While there are many things that can trigger its production, there are some easy things you can do to increase dopamine. One is to create a checklist and check off the completion of items. You can also smile, meditate, treat yourself to a favorite food, engage in a hobby, or just listen to calming music.

Oxytocin is the "love" hormone because it increases your sense of connection with others. Giving someone a compliment will increase oxytocin in you and in the other person. Any altruistic behavior such as contributing to someone's GoFundMe page, picking up trash in the park, or paying for the take-out order for the car behind you are all simple things you can do to raise your oxytocin. Spending time with a family member or a group of people you respect can also trigger higher levels of oxytocin in your body.

> *Dose*
> **Dopamine**
> **Oxytocin**
> **Serotonin**
> **Endorphins**

Serotonin is the "calming" neurotransmitter. Serotonin helps to create a sense of safety and control. Creating a list of things in your life that you are grateful for will increase your serotonin levels. Deliberately replacing negative thoughts with a positive affirmation or a more optimistic view of a situation will also increase serotonin.

Endorphins are the natural "pain-killers" in your body. They reduce your pain, help to relieve stress and enhance your sense of happiness. Exercise is the usual behavior recommended for raising your endorphins but there are other strategies as well. Exposure to natural light or getting more sleep will increase the endorphins in your body and will also boost serotonin levels. Laughing is another way to increase your endorphins.

Exercises

Taking back control

When your emotional brain, the limbic system and the reptilian brain has sounded the alarm and your amygdala has triggered the fight-or-flight response, your body is being flooded with cortisol and adrenaline. If you are going to manage a conflict effectively, you will need to take back control.

These exercises will help you to do that. If you practice them when you are not feeling stressed, it will be easier to implement them when you are faced with the difficult conversation.

1. A moment of mindfulness
    a. Set a timer for 1-2 minutes.
    b. Take some deep breaths. Deliberately slow down your breathing, taking in oxygen and fully expelling the carbon dioxide.
    c. Notice how the chair you are sitting on is supporting you, any sounds in your environment and how your feet are resting on the floor.
    d. Say to yourself, "For this moment, I am safe and I choose to be calm." You can repeat this several times.

2. Music for grounding
    a. Set a timer for 3-5 minutes.
    b. Find a peaceful, slow piece of music on your favorite app. This needs to be very peaceful. If you prefer, you can go to *www.conflictatworkbook.com/resources* where you can download a piece of music that is both peaceful and has the added advantage of a binaural hum in the background. This quiet hum helps to slow down your brainwaves so that you can achieve the alpha state more quickly.
    c. Focus your attention on the music, following its flow with your mind. If your mind wanders, which it will, gently bring it back to the music.
    d. While listening to this music, take some deep breaths. Deliberately slow down your breathing, taking in oxygen and fully expelling the carbon dioxide.

3. Loving faces
    a. Set a timer for 1-2 minutes.
    b. Find a picture of a loved one or a favorite pet on your smart phone.
    c. Take some deep breaths. Deliberately slow down your breathing, taking in oxygen, and fully expelling the carbon dioxide.
    d. Focus your attention on the picture in front of you. Allow yourself to feel the love and comfort this person or this pet brings you. If your mind wanders, which

it will, gently refocus your attention on the picture.

    e.   While gazing at the picture, say to yourself, "I am loved. I am worthy. I am safe."

4.   Self-hypnosis for confidence

    a.   Go to *www.conflictatworkbook.com/resources* and download the *Confidence for Difficult Conversations* recording.

    b.   Find a quiet place where you will not be disturbed and enjoy the recording. The recording is 22 minutes long so you will need to budget some time for this, but you will find that it is well worth it.

Increasing your DOSE

When you anticipate a difficult conversation, you can set yourself up for better results by engaging in exercises that will trigger the production of dopamine, oxytocin, serotonin, or endorphins. Spend some time on one or more of the following exercises.

1.   Dopamine:

    a.   Identify three small tasks that you can complete in the next 15 minutes. Write them on a post-it note with a little box that you can check off when you complete the task. These tasks should be small and easy to complete. As you complete the task, check each one off your list.

        For example:

        ☐   Call Gerald to confirm our lunch meeting.

        ☐   Get more paperclips for my desk.

        ☐   Choose what to cook for supper tonight.

    b.   Review your calendar for the previous two weeks. Note at least three things you accomplished during those two weeks. It doesn't matter whether these items are small things or just steps toward a larger goal. It all adds up and what is important is that you take time to notice and congratulate yourself on what you are getting done.

    c.   Set a timer for one minute. Place a pen or pencil between your teeth, horizontally and hold it there until the timer rings. When you do this, you are forcing your facial muscles into the same position as when you smile. Your brain registers the position of these muscles and responds as though you are truly smiling!

2.   Oxytocin:

    a.   Make a list of five things you can do to help someone else between now and the time you expect to have the difficult conversation. If possible, choose at least one thing you could do immediately before the conversation. It would be even better if you can think of something kind you could do for the person with whom you will be having the conversation. When you check the items off as complete, you get a two-for-one – an increase in both oxytocin and dopamine!

☐ _____
☐ _____
☐ _____
☐ _____
☐ _____

b.   Spend at least 15 minutes with someone you care about and enjoy being with. During this time, **do not** discuss the anticipated difficult conversation. Immerse yourself in the great feelings you get when you are with this person. If this is not possible, gaze at a picture of this person and think about how lucky you are to have this person in your life.

c.   If you have a pet, cuddle with it for 15 minutes. If you aren't with your pet, gaze at a picture of your furry friend and visualize how comforting it is to spend time with it.

d.   Write a short note to someone you care about and tell them how awesome they are. A handwritten note is best, but an email or text is better than not doing it at all.

e.   Give someone a sincere compliment. If there is no one available, write down a compliment that you will give to someone the next time you see them.

3.   Serotonin:
   a.   Set a timer for five minutes. Begin listing all the things in your life that you are grateful for. This will be easy at first but keep going. even when it gets trickier. Make the list as long as possible and include the little things like the hot coffee you drank this morning or the warm comfortable bed you slept in last night. Don't stop until the timer rings.

_____
_____
_____
_____
_____
_____

_____
_____
_____
_____
_____
_____
_____
_____
_____
_____
_____
_____
_____

b. Make a list of at least five things that are going well in your life.

1. _____
2. _____
3. _____
4. _____
5. _____

c. Imagine that the difficult conversation goes really well and then picture yourself feeling relieved and happy about the outcome after the conversation.

4. Endorphins:
   a. Go for a 10-minute brisk walk. If you are not able to do this, walk-in-place or find a staircase and go up and down a few times.

   b. There are a variety of 7-minute exercise routine applications available for both Android and iOS phones. Download one and use it. These are designed to require little equipment and to allow you to complete the routine anywhere.

   c. There are a variety of Dad-joke applications that you can download to your phone. Spend 3-5 minutes just reading some silly jokes.

   d. Listen to a funny podcast or find a service that features stand-up comedy. Sirius, Pandora, and many other services have them available. You can also find many videos or short clips from popular comedy shows on YouTube.com.

Deeper Thoughts

Set a timer for five minutes. Choose one of the following questions and write your answer. Continue to write until the timer rings.

1. The old adage states, "behind every dark cloud is a silver lining." What is the silver lining behind the difficult conversation you might be facing.
2. Imagine that you have had a difficult conversation with someone and it went surprisingly well. Describe what you did to contribute to that positive outcome and how you are now feeling about yourself and the other party to the conversation.
3. Imagine that you have assembled three people you trust and respect. They can be alive or have passed and you may or may not have ever actually met them. In your mind, place them in a semi-circle around you and introduce them to each other. Now, ask them to explain to you why this difficult conversation is not a personal threat to you and why you do not have to feel upset about having the conversation. Write out the conversation these three trusted mentors have with each other and with you.
4. Write a short story about the funniest thing that has ever happened to you or someone you know. Describe the context, what happened and how you felt after the event.
5. Write in great detail what it is that you value and respect about the person with whom you need to have a difficult conversation.

My thoughts:

_____

_____

_____

_____

_____

_____

_____

_____

_____

_____

What gets repeated, gets accepted: change your beliefs and you will change your outcomes.

Six
Mindset and the Power of "I am..."

Limiting beliefs

Our outcomes are often limited by our beliefs. Your subconscious is listening when you talk to yourself. It creates pictures which it then acts on. Your beliefs about how the world works and your place in the world sets boundaries around what is possible for you and influence how you think you should behave. These beliefs have been, and are being, shaped by what others tell you and what you tell yourself. You might not have direct control over what others tell you, but you do have control over what you accept from them. You also have control over what you say to yourself. When you change your stream of thought, you change your beliefs. If you change your beliefs, you can change your outcomes.

> *What you say to yourself matters!*

Negative thinking can become a self-fulfilling prophecy. To quote Henry Ford, "If you think you can do a thing or you can't do a thing, you are right." The words "I am..." are powerful words because they determine possibilities for you. They define you to yourself. If you tell yourself, "I'm not good at...," chances are your results will be less than optimal because that is the picture you have created in your head. You have told your subconscious, "Don't even try," and your subconscious is listening. As a result, you don't put in the effort needed for success.

If, instead, you change your self-talk dialogue to something more positive, you are painting a picture of success in your mind. With this picture, you have opened yourself to positive possibilities. Once again, your subconscious is listening and acting on the script you provide.

A self-affirmation statement is an antidote to negative thinking. By creating and repeating a positive statement to yourself, you can change an underlying belief that is negatively influencing your behavior. This change provides your subconscious with a new, healthier script to execute. A positive affirmation statement will build an automatic, and more productive, program that can moderate stress and, when faced with a difficult conversation, increase the probability of good outcomes.

To create an effective self-affirmation statement, there are some things to consider.

- Use first person – I;
- Use the present tense – for example, "I am..." or "I choose…"
- Make the statement positive. State what you do want, not what you don't want. For example, "I am confident and calm in a difficult conversation." Not, "I don't stutter and freeze up in a difficult conversation."

To re-write your belief and create that new, more positive script, the self-affirmation statement must be repeated - over and over - until it is fully integrated. The best way to do this is to place the statement in places where you see it several times a day. Each time you see it, you can pause and read the statement out loud or quietly to yourself. A post-it note beside your computer or on your refrigerator, the screen saver on your computer and smart phone, or written with a dry erase marker on your bathroom mirror, are all very good options.

Exercises

1. Since the way you describe yourself to yourself influences your behavior, it is important to become more aware of when you make "I am..." statements and what you tell yourself. You can use the space below or copy the format to a journal or a pad of paper.

   For the next three days, every time you say "I am…" to yourself or out loud, record it. If it is something positive, record it in the left-hand column. If it is negative, record it in the right-hand column.

Positive "I am ..." Statements	Negative "I am ..." Statements
Example: *I am good at this!*	Example: *I'm so tired.*

2. Rephrase each negative "I am…" statement you noted in the previous exercise, so that it either describes a feeling, instead of defining you, or it creates a positive message.

Negative "I am …" Statements	Rephrased Statements
Examples: *I'm so tired.* *I'm not good at spelling.*	Examples: *I feel tired.* *I am paying attention to my spelling and working on improving it.*

3. Choose a conflict that you are currently dealing with or you would like to resolve in the future.

   a. Write down your current "I am…" statement related to this conflict.

   Example: *I am so angry with Josh. If he didn't want to go out, why didn't he just tell me instead of being so negative all evening? I am fed up with this!*

   My current "I am …":

   _____

b. Create a positive statement about this conflict.

Example: *I choose to be calm when I talk with Josh. I am working on my listening skills and would like to understand Josh's perspective.*

My positive rephrase:

_____

c. We all have feelings about conflicts and their difficult conversations. For most people these feelings are uncomfortable. For others, they are intimidating, and for still others, they are simply a part of life to be dealt with when they surface. In the space below, describe how you feel about difficult conversations.

_____
_____
_____
_____
_____
_____
_____
_____
_____
_____
_____
_____
_____
_____
_____
_____
_____
_____
_____
_____

d. Review what you wrote in the previous exercise and identify any beliefs that may be underlying those feelings.

_____

_____

_____

_____

_____

_____

_____

_____

e. Given the beliefs you identified, write a self-affirmation statement you can use to counter those beliefs. Remember to use the guidelines for writing an effective self-affirmation statement.

Example:

Belief	Countering Self-Affirmation Statement
I am not good at conflict. I can't think clearly when I am in the middle of a conflict and so the other person always wins.	*I can breathe slowly, stay calm and think clearly during a conflict because a difficult discussion is not about winning or losing. It's about coming to a better outcome for both parties.*

Your self-affirmation statements:

Belief	Countering Self-Affirmation Statement

f.   A self-affirmation statement is only effective if you repeat it often. Check off the places you will put your self-affirmation statement to ensure that you see it and say it several times a day.

☐	Beside my computer.	☐	By the door on my way to my car.
☐	In my wallet.	☐	Beside the coffee machine.
☐	In a text message I sent to myself.	☐	On my screensaver (computer and/or smart phone)
☐	On my car dashboard.	☐	On my bathroom mirror.
☐	Other:	☐	Other:

Deeper Thoughts

Set a timer for five minutes. Choose one of the following questions and write down your answer. Continue writing until the timer rings.

1. When did you first notice that dealing with conflict was an intimidating experience? Who was involved in the conflict? What was said or done that made it intimidating?
2. How have you handled conflict in the past? How successful were you in resolving conflicts when you handled it this way?
3. In an earlier exercise, you identified a belief that might be making conflict harder for you. What other beliefs might you have about conflict? How are these beliefs affecting the way you handle conflict?
4. After practicing a self-affirmation statement daily for a week or more, what changes in your life have you noticed?
5. Listen to the *Confidence for Difficult Conversations* recording at: *www.conflictatworkbook.com/resources*. Immediately after the recording has ended, write any thoughts that have come to mind.

My thoughts:

_____

_____

_____

_____

_____

_____

_____

_____

_____

_____

_____

_____

_____

_____

It takes strength to be kind.

Seven
Kindness Wins

Challenging your instinct

When you are in the middle of a conflict at any level on the continuum, your first instinct is to protect yourself and your own interests. In doing so, you restore your sense of control and feeling of safety. Being kind might feel like you are giving in to the other person - the opposite of protecting your interests. You might be feeling like you are the victim and the other person is the villain. Therefore, they don't deserve your kindness. If you are kind, it's easy to equate kindness with being soft. It feels like you're going to be run over and the other person will take advantage of you.

The good news is that you can be kind and still protect your own interests. You do not have to be timid to be kind. Being assertive and being kind are not mutually exclusive terms. Being kind involves having compassion for the other person, being gentle in the words you choose, being considerate of the other person's needs, and finding ways to be helpful.

Kindness requires strength

When blended with assertiveness, being kind is not being soft. You can still protect your interests by knowing your boundaries. What can you offer to the other person without compromising your own needs? Kindness in conflict works when you know where the line is between truly serving others versus compromising your own needs.

> *Serving others should not compromise meeting your own needs. Kindness and assertiveness are not mutually exclusive terms.*

Assertiveness means that you act with self-confidence, are firm, positive and decisive. You can be all these things and still be kind. The challenge in blending kindness and assertivenss is that it takes strength. You must exercise a high degree of self-awareness to be decisive and firm, without tipping into being forceful, insistent, pushy or aggressive, or slipping into submissive behavior. This level of self-awareness takes a lot of work!

Dr. M. Paula Daoust

Benefits of kindness

Why should you be kind? There are three benefits. First, your body rewards you with oxytocin, the love hormone, when you behave altruistically. When the other person perceives your altruism toward them, they also get a burst of oxytocin with the result that they feel more connected to you. More importantly, it reduces their sense of threat. When you are being kind, fear is replaced by a growing sense of trust.

> *When you are kind, the true gift is to the giver.*

Second, kindness invokes the principle of reciprocity. We were all socialized to feel some pressure to return a kindness. We have ugly names for people who take and never return favors. If you are being helpful, the other person is more inclined to be helpful to you. The helpfulness you offer does not need to be directly related to the conflict. It might be something as simple as providing some needed information on a completely different project. The effort you invest is like putting money in the bank - it earns interest. In the case of conflict, you are building up social credit.

Third, it breaks the pattern of "tit-for-tat" by changing the dance between you and the other person. If you change your step while dancing the other person must follow with a change in their step. In the case of a conflict, it is hard to be mean to someone who is being kind to you. It's not impossible to continue being mean, but the other person will find it harder to justify aggressive behavior toward you.

The key to kindness is empathy

Kindness begins with empathy. As I said earlier, when we are in conflict, we often feel that the other person doesn't deserve our kindness. Any attempt to be kind under these conditions is going to come across as self-serving and manipulative. Kindness must come from the heart. To do this, we need to think differently about the other person.

There are two steps to preparing our hearts for kindness - seeing the other as a worthy human being and walking a mile in their shoes.

First, we need to remind ourselves of the other person's value and worthiness as a human being. What is it about this person that you respect and/or value? What you respect or value might be unconnected to the actual conflict but it will help you to see the other person in a more positive light.

In three different situations I landed on three different reasons for respecting others. In one case, I respected the way in which this person took care of his elderly parent. In another, it was the way in which she had triumphed over several traumatic events in her childhood and was able to become a positive, contributing citizen to society. In still a third situation, it was the person's artistic ability that drew my respect. In each of these situations, focusing on what I valued and respected in the other helped me to see the whole person that was in front of me. Although I didn't like them very much right now, I could still see them as worthy human beings and deserving of good things in their life.

Second, we must "walk a mile in their shoes." To muster enough empathy, we need to see the situation from their perspective. We don't have to agree with their perspective, but we need to at least understand why they might be feeling justified in their behavior.

Forgiveness

Sometimes anger and hurt are so deep that it feels impossible to be kind. Forgiveness is a gift you give to yourself so that you can let go of the hurt. If you are not able to forgive the other person you will feel the pain all over again each and every time you think of the injury they caused.

Forgiveness doesn't mean you forget the injury. It simply means that you let go of any resentment you might be feeling toward the other person so that you don't have to feel the pain over and over again. When you can let go of the hurt, you can move past it and begin the healing process. In this situation, kindness might consist of simply feeling some empathy for the other person's circumstances or seeing the good in them. It doesn't mean that the other person should not be held accountable for the injury they have caused, but it does mean that accountability is not extracted in a vengeful, punishing manner.

Exercises

Situation:

Provide a short description of a conflict situation and identify who the conflict is with. If you are continuing your work on a conflict used in other chapters, you can omit this section.

_____

_____

_____

1. Respect and value.

    a. What is it about this person that you can respect or that you value? List at least one thing but, if you can, list three or four things.

        _____

        _____

    b. If you were this other person, what might your motives be for your behavior. It is easy to think of negative, self-serving motives but push yourself to think about more positive motives. What might this person be feeling or thinking, given the information they might be operating with?

        _____

        _____

2. Take action

    a. List as many ways as you can think of in which you could be helpful to this other person. How could you demonstrate to this person that you care about them? Given what you respect or value in this person, what could you do to express that respect for them?

        1. _____

        2. _____

        3. _____

        4. _____

        5. _____

6. _____

7. _____

8. _____

9. _____

10. _____

b. It is just as important to know what you cannot do as it is to know what you can do. What will you not do? What, for you, represents giving up too much? For you, where is the boundary between assertiveness and being too passive?

1. _____

2. _____

3. _____

3. Forgiveness

If you find yourself ruminating on the hurt that the other person has caused you, you might want to consider working on forgiveness.

a. What makes it difficult to let go of the hurt?

_____

_____

b. In your own words, write a statement that acknowledges that your feelings are harming you and that ignoring or coping with them is not working:

_____

_____

c. In your own words, write a statement that recognizes that, while you do not agree with this person's actions, they are just trying to get by.

_____

_____

d. Reflect on how you have grown from this experience.

_____

_____

_____

_____

Deeper Thoughts

Set a timer for five minutes. Choose one of the following questions and write down your answer. Continue writing until the timer rings.

1. What is it about this situation that makes it hard to let go of my hurt and embrace being kind?
2. What am I likely to feel when I am consciously engaging in kind behavior toward this other person? Why?
3. How will I feel and respond if the other person does not return my kindness?
4. How might kindness contribute to resolving this particular conflict?
5. Is there something I need to forgive in order to be kind to this other person?

My thoughts:

The biggest challenge to communication is that we think we are speaking the same language.

Eight
Decoding and Using Language Effectively

Speaking in code

While we might think that we are speaking the same language as others, we actually speak in code. What I mean when I say that my boss is a challenge and what you think I said about my boss can be two very different things.

Adjectives and adverbs are usually code words. Our personal definition of an adjective or an adverb will often differ from that of others. These simple differences are the source of many conflicts. We often misunderstand the message because we have slightly different definitions for the same words and we don't realize it. Conflict can be avoided or resolved by taking four steps to break the code:

- Listen attentively.
- Check with the other person whether you understand their adverbs, adjectives, and metaphors correctly.
- Ask open-ended questions.
- Ask follow-up questions.

Sparks and triggers

Another issue that contributes to misunderstandings is that we are conditioned to respond in very predictable ways to specific words. We will respond negatively to some words – these are called triggers. They shut down thinking or induce resistance or withdrawal. There are other words to which we will respond positively – these are called sparks because they generate energy. If we use more sparks in our communication and avoid specific triggers, we can communicate more effectively.

Some common spark words or phrases are:

- Your name used early in a conversation and once or twice more in an extended conversation.
- You or your, you deserve ….
- Success, greatest, best, exclusive, perfect.

- I wonder, imagine, what if….
- Because.
- Perhaps, maybe, you might….
- Yes, and …, Yes, if ….
- You have probably already thought of this …, you probably already know….
- Easily, naturally, automatically.
- Help, support, guide, partner, team.
- New, surprising, instant, powerful, secret.
- Trust, love, like.

Some common trigger words or phrases:

Triggers	Some examples
Universals	Always, never, every, all, nobody, everybody, and everything.
Absolutes	Avoidable, certain, correct, defective, exact, harmless, incomplete, inevitable, irrefutable, literally, necessary, needless, obvious, superior, total, temporary, thorough, unavoidable, unequal, unimportant, universal, valid, worst, and wrong.
Why	Why did/didn't you…? Why are/aren't you…?
Minimizing	Just or at least
Demands	You need to…, you have to…, you should…, and, you must…
Negations	But or however
Don't	Don't take it personally. Don't be defensive. Don't take offense to this.

Body language

Body language is another way in which we communicate. It is our first language and when the messages from body language and symbolic language (words) are in conflict, we will trust the message provided through body language.

Managing Your Body Language

Learning how to manage your body language to avoid sending threatening messages is another strategy for reducing conflict. You will want to avoid the following:

- An exaggerated lean forward or stepping into the other party's personal space.
- Standing while the other person is sitting.
- Finger pointing and/or jabbing.
- Raising your hands above your waist when there is tension in the environment.
- Bared teeth or pursed lips.
- Clenched fists.
- Crossing your arms.
- Laughing or grinning at the other person.
- A fixed stare.

Reading Other's Body Language

In addition to managing your own non-verbal communications, you can also learn to notice the other party's body language. Whenever there are signs that they are feeling fear or a threat, you can take steps to de-escalate the situation. Signs that the other person is feeling threatened or is alarmed might include some of the following. A single gesture or behavior cannot be accurately interpreted. When two or more of these gestures co-occur, you might want to take note and adjust your behavior:

- A change in volume of their voice – getting louder or significantly quieter.
- A change in pitch of their voice.
- Quickened or slower and measured speech.
- Physical changes such as a flushed face, breathing faster, swallowing frequently, trembling, pacing, tapping, or muscle tension.

Increasing confidence through posture

Non-verbal behaviors communicate to others, but they also communicate to our subconscious. You can use a power pose to increase your self-confidence in anticipation of a conflict or another stressful event.

Furthermore, instead of sinking into your chair with arms and legs crossed and shoulders hunched over, you can consciously choose a more confident posture. To do this you can take up more space by sitting up straight, with your head up, and your hands resting on the arms of the chair. In doing this, you deliver the message to your subconscious that you are relaxed and in control.

Communicating with stories

Finally, stories are a powerful tool for delivering a message. When you tell a story, it creates images in the other person's mind. They don't just hear the story, but also live the story as you tell it. This engages the emotional brain. Additionally, your brains are synchronized while you are sharing the story and they are listening. As they listen, they are extracting the message and making it their own. With the emotional brain engaged, changes in behavior are more likely to occur. Here are some things to consider when telling a story to create empathy:

- The listener should be able to relate to the central person of the story, the protagonist. They should be able to visualize themselves in the story. The protagonist might be you or it might be an example of someone else who is dealing with a similar conflict. If the protagonist is you, your story might be about a past conflict or the current conflict.
- Clarify the goal or intention of the protagonist. What is it the protagonist wants or intends to do?
- What is getting in the way of the protagonist achieving their goal? Describe the barrier, complication, or obstacle that the protagonist must deal with to accomplish their goal.
- Describe the protagonist's feelings in response to encountering the barrier, complication, or obstacle.
- Finish with the protagonist pushing through to a resolution or with the hope that it will be possible to achieve a positive resolution.
- Avoid using too many details, facts, or figures.
- Add some sensory details so the listener can better picture the experience.

Exercises

Decoding the message.

If you practice these exercises enough, you will become sensitized to the presence of code words such as adjectives, adverbs, or metaphors in a conversation. When you are chatting with someone, you don't need to clarify every code word used. However, sensitivity to code words can be a useful tool for avoiding misunderstandings, especially if there is any tension in the conversation. Instead of assuming that you know what the other person is communicating, you will be reminded to check your understanding.

1. Noticing code words:

    a. Find a 2-3 minute video clip of two or more people engaged in a conversation. If you search YouTube for "Friends" or "The Middle" you will find many examples that you can use.

    b. Record each of the adverbs, adjectives, or metaphors used by any participant in the conversation.

    c. Listen to the same video clip again and see if you can catch any code words that you missed the first time.

    d. Select three of the code words and describe what you believe the speaker meant by each word.

    e. Show the video clip to a partner. After watching the clip, ask the partner what they think the speaker meant for each of the code words you selected. How close was their understanding to yours? Keep in mind that small differences can make for big misunderstandings!

Code words I heard the first time listening to the video clip	Additional code words I heard the second time I listened to the video clip

Code Word	What I think the word means	What my partner thinks the word means

2. Brief clarifying exercise:
   Note: *It is best to practice this exercise in a non-stressful conversation.*

   a. Ask someone to participate in this exercise with you.
   b. Set a timer for five minutes.
   c. Choose a topic in which the other person has a strong interest.
   d. Ask your partner to begin explaining why they are interested in the topic. Note any adjectives, adverbs, and metaphors your partner uses.
   e. Check your understanding of the other person's use of an adjective, adverb, or metaphor. Examples might include:
      • "When you said you were angry, what did you mean by that?"
      • "You said you were excited about your football team's win, how did that feel?"
      • "How do you know you are frustrated? Where do you feel it?"
      • "What does 'feeling proud' mean to you?"
   f. Listen carefully to your partner's answers and your clarifying questions, and follow-up with additional questions.

Using more effective language patterns.

Whenever possible, you want to integrate words into your sentences that evoke positive responses. You also want to avoid triggering unnecessary resistance or withdrawal from the conversation.

1. Using spark words.

For each of the following scenarios, write down briefly what you could say and include at least three of the sparks described in the overview.
(Suggested answers are available on page 158.)

    a. You would like a team-member to correct some errors on a report which they prepared for you.
    b. A colleague has asked you to cover the phones while they take a break. This is the third break they have taken this morning!
    c. You must introduce a change in a procedure and you expect that the change will be unpopular with your team.
    d. Your direct-report is ten minutes late getting to work. This has become a pattern.
    e. You need to assign someone to clean the break room refrigerator.

	Sentence with at least three spark words
a.	
b.	
c.	
d.	
e.	

2. Eliminating trigger words.
   Re-write each of the following sentences by eliminating trigger words while maintaining the same meaning.
   (Suggested answers are available on page 158.)

a.   I was just going to get to it. You never give me a chance to get my work done.

   _____

   _____

b.   You should have taken more time when you entered the information in this report. It's all wrong and now I will have to correct it.

   _____

   _____

c.   Why didn't you check the report before you submitted it? There are several avoidable errors in it.

   _____

   _____

d.   Don't take this personally but everybody is complaining that your cologne is giving them a headache.

   _____

   _____

e.   Every day is the same thing. It's obvious that no one cares about this company as much as I do!

   _____

   _____

Awareness of body language.

When you are in the middle of a conflict, you might engage in behavior that triggers defensiveness in the other party. This can happen because all your attention is focused on the issue which is upsetting you and you will naturally engage in behavior that will maximize your safety and increase your dominance.

You might also be communicating that you feel threatened. This could be a signal to the other person that they might get the upper hand by increasing their dominant behaviors.

1. Awareness of your body language when dealing with conflict.
   Consider a conflict you were engaged in the past. Complete the following assessment and then, without showing them the scores you gave yourself, ask others how they would score your behavior on each item.

   0 = Never; **2** = Occasionally; **3** = Sometimes;
   4 = Frequently; **5** = Always or almost always.

	Items	Self Score	Other 1	Other 2
1.	Exaggerated lean forward or stepping into other person's space.			
2.	Standing while the other person is sitting.			
3.	Finger pointing and/or jabbing.			
4.	Raising your hands above your waist while in conflict.			
5.	Bared teeth or pursed lips.			
6.	Clenched fists.			
7.	Laughing or grinning at the other person.			
8.	Change in volume of voice – louder or much quieter.			
9.	Quickened or slower, measured speech.			
10.	Physical changes: flushed face, breathing faster, swallowing frequently, trembling, pacing, tapping, or muscle tension.			
	Total Score			

2. Awareness of the other person's body language when dealing with conflict.
   In the first column, score how often over the last year you have observed others display each item.

   0 = Never; **2** = Occasionally; **3** = Sometimes;
   4 = Frequently; **5** = Always or almost always.

   In the second column, score the degree to which each item bothers you when you see it in a conflict you are involved in.

   0 = Not at all; **2** = Somewhat bothered; **3** = Very bothered.

	Items	Frequency of observation	How much it bothers me
1.	Exaggerated lean forward or stepping into other person's space.		
2.	Standing while the other person is sitting.		
3.	Finger pointing and/or jabbing.		
4.	Raising hands above the waist while in conflict.		
5.	Bared teeth or pursed lips.		
6.	Clenched fists.		
7.	Laughing or grinning at the other person.		
8.	Change in volume of voice – louder or much quieter.		
9.	Quickened or slower, measured speech.		
10.	Physical changes:flushed face, breathing faster, swallowing frequently, trembling, pacing, tapping, or muscle tension.		
	Total Score		

3. After reviewing the scores on the previous assessment, identify which items scored at 2 or 3. Describe strategies you might use to negate the effect of other's body language on you.

_____

_____

_____

_____

_____

_____

_____

_____

_____

Power pose

In this exercise, you will have an opportunity to experience the benefit of engaging in a power pose. When you anticipate you are going to have a conversation that could become tense, you can find somewhere private and take two minutes to practice the exercise.

1. Basic Power Pose

   a. Set a timer for two minutes.
   b. Stand in front of a mirror if possible.
   c. Place your feet approximately shoulder-width apart, throw your shoulders back, lift your head, and place your hands on your hips.
   d. Stare into your eyes and repeat a self-affirmation statement. If you don't have a personal affirmation statement you can say something like, "I can be calm, confident and think clearly throughout this conversation. I want a good result for both myself and [name of other person]."

Communicating with a story

Using stories in a conflict is most effective when you have an inventory of stories to draw from. Ideally, you will use stories from your own experience but, when that is not possible, you can borrow a story. Fortunately, the media gives you many examples you can use. Sit-coms are an especially rich source of conflict stories.

Watch an episode and, using the tips described in this chapter, write a short story that ends with a positive, healthy resolution (you might have to change the ending from the one in the show). Create an inventory of four or five of these stories.

Deeper Thoughts

Set a timer for five minutes. Choose one of the following questions and write down your answer. Continue writing until the timer rings.

1. Now that I am aware of code words, what impact do I think these words have had on past conflicts? How will I ensure that they do not cause unnecessary misunderstandings in the future?
2. Where in my life can I use more spark words? Which of the spark words am I already using consistently and which ones would I like to use more frequently? What difference might they make in particular relationships?
3. How frequently am I using trigger words in my conversations? What can I do to minimize my use of trigger words? In the past, what impact has the use of these words had on my relationships?
4. What did I learn after comparing my scores on the body language assessment with the scores others gave me? How do I feel about the comparison? Is there any behavior that I would like to change?
5. Recognizing that some body language behaviors by others are bothering me, what might I do so that they don't have as much impact on me during a conflict.

My thoughts:

_____

_____

_____

_____

_____

_____

_____

_____

_____

_____

_____

_____

Start rewarding the behavior you do want and STOP rewarding the behavior you don't want!

Nine
Behavioral Science and Conflict

Conditioning

If the same thing keeps happening, it may be a conditioned response. You can notice where conditioning may be the culprit in your own or others' patterned behavior. There are two kinds of conditioning that could be at work: classical and operant conditioning.

Classical conditioning occurs when a neutral stimulus is frequently paired with a reflexive response. With enough pairings, you begin to respond to the neutral event with that reflexive response. For example, if you consistently get a headache in your office when a co-worker wears a certain cologne, after enough pairings, your headache will begin soon after you enter the office, even before your co-worker arrives.

In the workplace, operant conditioning is more common than classical conditioning. Operant conditioning can be summarized as an A-B-C sequence: antecedent, behavior, consequence. Something prompts or leads to the behavior. This is the antecedent. The behavior occurs and a consequence follows. The consequence is either rewarding and leads to the behavior being repeated or the consequence is a punisher which leads to the behavior decreasing. Praise, awards, bonuses, and reprimands are all built on operant conditioning.

The challenge in operant conditioning is that what one person finds rewarding could be punishing for someone else. A supervisor thinks she is rewarding the good work of an employee by giving them an award in front of the whole team. To her dismay, the quality of the employee's work drops off soon after the award presentation. When this happens, it is easy to argue that rewards don't work. If you look closer, however, you might discover that the employee is terribly shy, which made the public presentation embarrassing or uncomfortable. What was intended as a reward was experienced as a punisher.

> *What one person finds rewarding can be experienced as a punisher by another.*

Using operant conditioning

If you don't like the response you are getting, in yourself or others, you can change the consequences. You want to start rewarding the behavior you do want and stop rewarding the behavior you don't want. To do this, you will need to understand what the individual in question experiences as rewarding. Often, if you simply look at the sequence of behavior, you can identify what is currently rewarding the unwanted behavior.

For example, when team members tell Terry, their supervisor, that something can't be done, his standard response is, "If you can't do it, I'll find someone who can." It isn't long before no one says no to Terry's requests. His threats are rewarded with what appears to him to be compliance. Unfortunately, Terry's projects regularly go over budget and have major quality problems.

If Terry's team wants him to change his threatening behavior, they will need to step up and stop rewarding him with their short-term compliance. If Terry wants to get better performance from his team, he will need to look at the pattern of outcomes he is currently getting and notice that the compliance he is getting is short-term only. The reward for his threatening behavior is more apparent than real! If what he really wants is quality work and timely results, he will need to pivot from his punishing threats to rewarding positive outcomes.

If you want certain behavior to occur more often, reward it. Rewards can be as simple as a head nod, a smile, or praise. More tangible rewards can include a gift card, an award, or maybe even a high-profile project. To be effective, the reward needs to follow the behavior as closely as possible and it needs to be something that the other person finds pleasant.

> *If you want a behavior to occur more often, reward it.*

Rewards can also be the cessation of an unpleasant event. For example, when you exit the building, you no longer hear the annoying fire-drill alarm. Your compliance to the fire-drill routine by going outside is rewarded by relief from the loud sound.

There is one more thing you need to be aware of when using rewards and that is the condition of habituation. Our brains crave variety and when the same reward is offered too often, it loses its ability to reinforce the behavior. For this reason, you need to vary the rewards you use.

The problem with punishment

This brings us to another critical issue - the use of punishment. In the short-term, punishment appears to be effective and that is exactly why it is seductive. When you are reprimanded, you might increase your rate of compliant behavior, but it comes at the cost of quality and creative problem-solving. This happens because a reprimand, or any other punisher, arouses the fight-or-flight response with the accompanying side-effects of reduced cognitive functioning.

You might observe increased activity, but errors are more likely and creative thought is hindered, if not prevented altogether. When threatened with punishment, you are more likely to choose the safe option rather than taking a risk with a different, and perhaps more effective or efficient approach. You will make this safe choice even if your expect that it will only be marginally effective.

In addition, punishment damages work relationships and builds up resentment, both of which have a myriad of negative consequences. If team members don't trust you or don't like you, they are unlikely to put in any extra effort or to help you when you need it.

Finally, over time, people become desensitized to a punisher. To get the same increase in activity, you will find yourself needing to increase the intensity of the punisher. In the workplace, it isn't long before you run out of ways to increase the intensity of your punisher. When you get to the end of punishing options, you might find yourself recommending the ultimate workplace punisher - termination.

For all of these reasons, it is wise to avoid using punishment to change behavior. The change won't last and there are problematic side effects.

Generalizing from one situation to another

Associated with the A-B-C is stimulus generalization which occurs when you respond to similar events in a similar way. For example, if in the past you proposed a new idea to your team and they responded with many difficult questions, you might hesitate in the future to present your ideas to your team or to any other team. Your unpleasant experience in the one circumstance has been generalized to an expectation of unpleasantness in any other similar event.

Stimulus generalization is responsible for both good and bad behavior patterns in the workplace. When a customer receives great service, they assume that their next encounter with your organization will be positive and they continue doing business with you. Obviously, the opposite is also true.

If you believe stimulus generalization is happening - and is causing problems for you or your organization - you will want to put a systematic program of reinforcement in place to counter it. Training programs that teach customer service employees to listen, ask probing questions and to respond proactively to customer problems are an example of a systematic program for countering or preventing stimulus generalization as a result of poor service.

Extinction of behavior

While using punishment to reduce unwanted behavior is not recommended, there is a tool that you can use that does not offer the same risk of unwanted side-effects. Behaviors will decrease or disappear when they are no longer rewarded. This is referred to as extinction. Extinction can be quite effective in eliminating unwanted behavior. A co-worker might have a pattern of sharing gossip with you. If you find it uncomfortable to listen to it and want the pattern to stop, you need to remove the reward for that behavior. Walking away or finding something to be busy with while the co-worker is talking will remove the reward of an audience. Do it often enough and your co-worker will find another audience or, if that is not available, stop sharing gossip altogether.

There is one caveat in the use of extinction. Before a behavior that is no longer being rewarded will disappear, there is usually a short increase in the frequency or intensity of the behavior. This is called an extinction burst. If you expect an extinction burst, you will know that at first your co-worker will stop by your desk even more frequently for a short period of time or will have reasons why you need to hear this particular, juicy piece of gossip. Your co-worker will probably try new strategies for engaging you in the gossip like sending you instant messages or calling you on the telephone. If you give in to the extinction burst, you will have taught your co-worker to be more persistent or intense and that is not a good thing. If you decide to use extinction, you must anticipate the extinction burst and be prepared to weather it. If you do, the behavior will subside and eventually disappear.

A second concern with the use of extinction is spontaneous recovery. After a period of time in which the behavior has been successfuly extinguished, it can suddenly re-occur. If you give in to this spontaneous re-occurrence by rewarding the behavior, the old pattern will reassert itself even stronger than it was before. If, instead, you are prepared for spontaneous recovery and resist rewarding the behavior, it will disappear again - and probably for good this time.

Exercises

1. Applying the A-B-C sequence.

   To help you see the application of antecedents, behaviors, and consequences, review the following scenarios and write down your answers to the questions. (*You can check your answers on page 159.*)

   a. Gerrard needed some additional office supplies. Instead of just walking down the hall and asking the supply clerk for what he needed, he chose to follow company procedure and fill out the appropriate forms. Surprisingly, when he submitted his request, it was rejected.

Antecedent	Behavior	Consequence (circle one)
		Reward **Punisher**

   What do you predict Gerrard will do the next time he needs supplies?

   _____

   _____

   If the organization wants employees to use the forms for requesting supplies, what might they do differently?

   _____

   _____

   b. Helena stayed late to make sure that she could submit her report to Ray-Anne in time. The next day, Ray-Anne told Helena that her work should have been completed during regular work hours and that she would not be paid overtime.

Antecedent	Behavior	Consequence (circle one)
		Reward Punisher

What do you predict Helena will do the next time a report has to be submitted?

_____

_____

If Rae-Anne wants Helena's best effort on future reports, how might she have handled this situation differently?

_____

_____

c. Arthur was having trouble closing a sale. A friend told him he was trying too hard and to listen more and talk less the next time he met with the customer. He tried this approach on his next visit and got the sale.

Antecedent	Behavior	Consequence (circle one)
		Reward Punisher

What do you predict Arthur will do the next time he meets with his customer?

_____

_____

How might stimulus-generalization be applied to this situation to ensure continued success as a salesperson?

_____

_____

d. Lilly was frustrated with the constant mess in the break room. She had complained about it in staff meetings several times but nothing improved. She decided to put a plan into place. Every time she went into the break room, she would find something that was clean and take a picture of it. She then posted the picture on the bulletin board with a simple "Thank you" post-it note attached.

Antecedent	Behavior	Consequence (circle one)
		Reward Punisher

What impact do you predict Lilly's plan will have on the cleanliness of the break room?

_____

_____

Why do you think Lilly's plan will have the effect you described?

_____

_____

e. Laird consistently arrived at meetings without the files he needed to participate fully. As a result, Erin, the team leader, often had to postpone the discussion of difficult decisions to the next meeting.

Antecedent	Behavior	Consequence (circle one)
		Reward Punisher

What impact is the postponement of discussions likely to have on Laird's future behavior?

_____

_____

What might Erin do if she wants to break the current pattern of behavior?

_____

_____

f. Micah was the leader of a project team that didn't work well together and members also did not like being questioned about their progress or decisions. Micah decided that he would follow every answer he got to his questions with a positive comment about some aspect of the answer.

Antecedent	Behavior	Consequence (circle one)
		Reward **Punisher**

What impact do you think Micah's positive comments will have on team member's willingness to be questioned?

_____

_____

Why do you think so?

_____

_____

g. Jonas asked Alice for some information and was told that she didn't have it. A week later it became evident that Alice did have the information and chose not to share it. Jonas contacted Alice's supervisor to complain about the lack of co-operation on Alice's part.

Antecedent	Behavior	Consequence (circle one)
		Reward **Punisher**

What impact, and for how long, do you think Jonas' complaint will have on Alice's behavior?

_____

_____

What else might Jonas have tried to improve Alice's willingness to share information?

_____

_____

h. Things got a little tense in a meeting and Cynthia raised her voice and pointed her finger at a teammate. This was not the first time Cynthia engaged in this kind of behavior. Nate, her supervisor, told Cynthia to calm down and, in front of the team, reminded Cynthia that she was not being helpful.

Antecedent	Behavior	Consequence (circle one)
		Reward **Punisher**

What impact would Nate's actions have on Cynthia's behavior and on their relationship?

_____

_____

Why do you think so?

_____

_____

i. Dana had to take some time off to care for a family member who was sick. As a result, her work fell behind and this was negatively affecting the team's productivity. Without saying a word to anyone, Emma quietly stepped in and started processing some of the files assigned to Dana.

Antecedent	Behavior	Consequence (circle one)
		Reward **Punisher**

What impact would Emma's behavior have on the team and on her relationship with Dana?

_____

_____

Why do you think so?

_____

_____

j.   Gina, the supervisor, was noticing that members of her team were leaving early. It would be different members on different days and it was usually not more than 10 minutes early but the lost work time was beginning to have an impact on the team's productivity. She decided that she would walk around the office at quitting time every day and exchange some small talk with each person who was still in the office.

Antecedent	Behavior	Consequence (circle one)
		Reward **Punisher**

What impact do you think Gina's evening tour would have on her team's behavior?

_____

_____

Why do you think so?

_____

_____

2.   Applying behavior analysis to your conflict.

Consider a conflict situation that is familiar to you. It might be one that you are dealing with now or one from the past, or it might be a situation that you have observed.

a. Briefly describe the situation.

_____

_____

_____

_____

b. Antecedent: What led up to the situation? What was the context?

_____

_____

c. Behavior: What was the behavior? What was done? Be specific in describing the behavior that followed the antecedent.

_____

_____

_____

_____

d. Consequence: What followed the behavior? What result did the behavior create?

_____

_____

e. How might the consequence be changed to create a better result?

_____

_____

_____

_____

Deeper Thoughts

Set a timer for five minutes. Choose one of the following questions and write your answer down. Continue writing until the timer rings.

1. How might I be accidentally rewarding behaviors I don't want?
2. How might I use praise or rewards to increase behavior I do want?
3. How might the use of punishment be suppressing behavior I do want or increasing behavior I don't want?
4. Is stimulus-generalization affecting any of my behavior and, if so, what strategies could I put in place to change it?
5. How might I use extinction to change a behavior in myself or others? When I use extinction, what strategy will I use to weather the extinction burst?

My thoughts:

Access your inner resources to resolve conflict easier.

Ten
Be Hypnotic!

Using self-hypnosis

All hypnosis is self-hypnosis. It is all about mind control but it is you who is doing the controlling. Hypnosis is a natural state that you go into and out of every day. Watching a movie, thinking through a problem while driving, or just daydreaming, are all hypnotic trances. A trance is simply focused attention with temporary exclusion of other stimuli. When you are in a hypnotic trance, you can better access your inner resources - your creative subconscious - and this has some advantages when working with conflict.

> *All hypnosis is self-hypnosis. It is a natural state that you go in and out of many times a day.*

When in a hypnotic trance, you can slow your beta brainwaves from the more active, alert 20-30 Hz per second to a pattern that is at the margin between alpha and beta waves, somewhere between 11-15 Hz per second. This slower cycling allows the brain to take advantage of both rational, conscious thought and the creative, problem-solving of subconscious processing. When dealing with conflict, this combination of alpha and beta states can be a major asset in allowing you to think clearly and to see solutions that might not otherwise be obvious to you.

There are several tools that can help you to achieve advantageous states for problem-solving and managing conflict. Mindful meditation, guided visualization, progressive relaxation, neurolinguistic programming, and self-hypnosis can all be used to relieve stress and to access a resourceful state.

Any of these tools can be used proactively prior to a difficult conversation to become calm. Although more challenging, if you practice, you can also use them in the middle of a difficult conversation to help you be fully present in the moment. My recommendation for you is to use your choice of these tools as you plan your conversation or immediately prior to entering the difficult conversation.

Irrational beliefs

Hypnosis is indeed a natural state and one form of trance tends to be pervasive across many settings and influences much of your behavior. That trance is built on irrational beliefs and, as Albert Ellis argued, these beliefs can cause unnecessary suffering. Everyone acquires some of these beliefs. It would be unusual if, after a scan of Ellis' twelve irrational beliefs, none of them resonated with you. Provided a belief is not so firmly entrenched in your thinking that it eliminates any flexibility and completely dictates your actions, it is not a problem. In some cases, the belief might even push you to better performance.

It is useful to understand to what degree irrational beliefs are influencing your behavior. If it is a mild influence, then just knowing what it is can help you to use it to your advantage. When the belief becomes extreme, however, misery will follow. If you are operating under a deeply held irrational belief, then it would be to your advantage to take steps to challenge it. You can get a quick assessment at: *www.conflictatworkbook.com/resources.*

Albert Ellis' list of irrational beliefs are:

1. I need to feel love and approval from those significant to me, and I must avoid disapproval from any source.
2. To feel happy and worthwhile, I must achieve, succeed at whatever I do, and make no mistakes.
3. People should always do the right thing. When they behave obnoxiously, unfairly, or selfishly, they must be blamed and punished.
4. Things must be the way I want them to be; otherwise, life will be intolerable.
5. My unhappiness is caused by things outside of my control, so there is little I can do to feel any better.
6. I must worry about things that could be dangerous, unpleasant, or frightening; otherwise, they might happen.
7. I can be happier by avoiding life's difficulties, unpleasantness, and responsibilities.
8. We absolutely need someone stronger or greater than ourselves to rely on.
9. Events in my past are causing my problems and they continue to influence my feelings and behaviors now.
10. I should become upset when other people have problems and feel unhappy when they are sad.
11. I shouldn't have to feel discomfort and pain. I can't stand them and must avoid them at all cost.

12. Every problem should have an ideal solution, and it is intolerable when one can't be found.

Principles of influence

Another form of trance we all experience is Cialdini's six principles of influence. They are hypnotic in that they change behavior at a subconscious level. When used ethically in a conflict, they can reduce tension and increase the probability of finding a solution that works for both you and the other person. In conflict, if one person loses, no one can win. Using a combination of these principles can open discussion in a healthier manner and allow a win-win solution to emerge.

The six principles are:

- *Reciprocity* – people expect to repay in kind.
  If you do something to be helpful or say something positive to the other person, they will feel some pressure to return the kindness to you.

- *Scarcity* – people want what is not readily available.
  Loss aversion tells us that if a person feels that you are restricting their access to something, they will resist you. Reframe a change in terms of a gain and you will get more cooperation, particularly if the gain is not readily available to everyone.

- *Social proof (consensus)* – people follow the lead of similar others. Drawing attention to people who are cooperating with you or are agreeing to something will improve the probability of getting an agreement from the person with whom you are in conflict. This is especially true if the other people you are pointing out have something in common with the person with whom you are in conflict.

- *Authority* – people defer to experts or people in charge.
  Using information from a source that the other person deems credible will help you to get agreement on an issue.

- *Consistency or commitment* – people act in ways that demonstrate personal alignment.
  People will tend to fulfill written, public, or voluntary commitments. If you ask the other person to write down a commitment or decision in their own handwriting, there is a high probability that they will honor whatever they wrote. You can accomplish the same thing if you ask the person to explain their decision or a commitment to someone else or to announce it to a group.

- *Liking* – people will cooperate with similar others or with people who demonstrate that they respect or care about them.
  A powerful way to resolve a conflict is to show clearly that you care for and/or respect the other person. Being liked is almost irresistible because it minimizes the sense of threat. People who like you don't intend to harm you!

Exercises

1. Accessing your inner resources.

   a. Choose a conflict that you are dealing with now, you have dealt with in the past, or you expect to deal with in the near future.
      Conflict:

      _____

      _____

      _____

   b. Describe the details of the conflict, particularly your feelings around the conflict.

      _____

      _____

      _____

      _____

   c. Choose a mindful meditation, guided visualization, progressive relaxation, neuro-linguistic programming, or a self-hypnosis for calmness or confidence recording of your choice.

      You can find many options using an application on your smart phone or you can download the "*Confidence mindset for difficult conversations*" which I have recorded for you at: *www.conflictatworkbook.com/resources.*

   d. Listen to one of these recordings, then answer the following questions:

      Do you feel calmer now than you did before the recording?   Yes / No
      If **yes,** *describe this feeling of calmness. Where in your body is it located? Is it in a small space or is it as big as you or even bigger? If it had a color, what color would it be? Can you move it around or is it locked in place? If it had a temperature, would it be hot or cold? If you could taste or smell it, what would it taste like or smell like? If it had a sound, what would it sound like?*

      _____

      _____

      _____

      _____

_____

_____

_____

_____

Has your perspective on the conflict changed in any way?   Yes / No
If yes, describe your new perspective.

_____

_____

_____

_____

e. Take the other person's perspective and explain how they might be feeling justified in their behavior and/or be feeling like the victim in this conversation.

_____

_____

_____

_____

_____

_____

_____

_____

_____

f. Explain how you feel about this conflict now:

_____

_____

_____

_____

_____

_____

2. Challenging irrational beliefs.

    a. Complete the self-assessment at: *www.conflictatworkbook.com/resources*

    b. List those of the twelve irrational beliefs for which you scored a 6 or higher on the chart below.

    c. For each irrational belief you recorded in the chart, write a statement that refutes the belief. Use your own words. The worksheet offers you two examples of refuting statements. You will only need one but it needs to be right for you. For example, if you scored high on the statement, "To feel happy and worthwhile I must achieve and succeed at whatever I do, and make no mistakes," your refuting statement might be, "Everyone makes mistakes and if I make a mistake, I'm just being human" or, "People will see me as worthwhile even if I do make a mistake."

	Irrational Belief	Refuted Statement
1.		
2.		
3.		

    d. After writing your refuting statement(s), read the words three times to yourself.

For 14 consecutive days, begin and end each day day by reading your refuting statement(s) three times. Record each time you practice your refuted statement(s) in the log below. This will help you stay accountable to yourself. If at any time the statement(s) no longer sound right to you, edit the statement(s) so that it continues to inspire you.

Day	Morning ✔	Bedtime ✔
1		
2		
3		
4		
5		
6		
7		
8		
9		
10		
11		
12		
13		
14		

e. Go to *www.conflictatworkbook.com/resources* and listen to the *"Challenging Irrational Beliefs"* recording. Describe how you feel about the irrational belief after listening to the recording.

_____

_____

_____

_____

_____

_____

_____

_____

Using the principles of influence.

a. Choose a conflict that you are dealing with now, have dealt with in the past, or you expect to deal with in the near future.
    Conflict: _____

    _____

b. Choose at least three of Cialdini's six principles of influence. For each principle, describe what actions you could take for the conflict you have identified.

Principle	Action I can take

Deeper Thoughts

Set a timer for five minutes. Choose one of the following questions and write down your answer. Continue writing until the timer rings.

1. Given the specific conflicts that I am dealing with in my life, how might I use any of the self-hypnosis experiences - mindful meditation, guided visualization, progressive relaxation, neurolinguistic programming, or self-hypnosis for calmness or confidence - to help me get better results and improve my relationship with the other person.

2. Now that you are familiar with Albert Ellis' twelve irrational beliefs, identify how these beliefs have influenced your past behavior?

3. How can you make any of the twelve irrational beliefs work for you to improve your performance? What actions can you take to ensure that these beliefs don't slip into becoming a problem for you?

4. Which of Cialdini's six principles of influence do you use consistently? How might you increase the use of these natural patterns of behavior to improve your relationships at work?

5. Which of the six principles have you not used consistently in the past? How might you use them more to influence behavior at work?

My thoughts:

_____

_____

_____

_____

_____

_____

_____

_____

_____

_____

_____

_____

How can I ensure that [the problem] does not improve?

Eleven
Aiki Breakthrough Change Method

Being stuck

Some conflicts are just very hard to resolve. You try this and you try that - and you still don't make any progress. Or you think you have the issue resolved and it shows up again later.

When people find themselves stuck like this, out of frustration they often do exactly the wrong thing and believe it's right. The reason we do the wrong thing is because the frustration provokes a fight-or-flight response and, while in this state, we tend to focus our energy on escaping from the problem.

> *When people are stuck, out of frustration, they often do the wrong thing and believe it is right.*

Doing something different: the Aiki approach

Instead of trying to make the situation go away, it's time to do something very different. The Aiki approach redirects our energy from escape toward being present in the problem. It engages the problem very differently by asking: "How can I ensure that [the problem] never improves?"

Changing your focus toward maintaining or strengthening the problem is counter-intuitive. Because it's not rational your conscious, logical brain steps out of the problem-solving mode and allows your more creative subconscious to control your thinking. This allows truth-telling to emerge. The consciously unacknowledged or unrecognized sources of the problem surface in the ideas for maintaining or strengthening the problem.

Steps in the Aiki Breakthrough Change model

1. Identify exactly what conflict you want to resolve.
2. List at least ten things you could do to ensure that the conflict does not get resolved, or maybe gets worse.

3. Identify which behaviors on the list you have or are currently engaging in.
4. Create a plan to help you to stop engaging in these behaviors.
5. Review the list for potential items that, if reversed, could be added to your plan.
6. Execute the plan!

The power of the Aiki Breakthrough Change model is that when you review your list of ideas, you often quickly recognize some behaviors that you are currently engaging in. Although you hadn't consciously acknowledged or even recognized them previously, once said, it is hard to ignore them. When you take action to stop engaging in these behaviors, you will have a successful strategy for resolving the conflict.

> *The Aiki Breakthrough Change model induces truth-telling. Once something is said, it's hard to ignore.*

Making the list will also stimulate some creative ideas for resolving the conflict that might not have occurred to you before doing the Aiki brainstorm. The value of the Aiki Breakthrough Change method is that it helps you to break through your own trapped way of thinking.

Exercises

1. Applying the Aiki Breakthrough Change Method to scenarios:

    For each of the following scenarios, complete the exercise as if this was your own conflict. Just let your imagination fly when coming up with possible strategies for making sure the conflict is not resolved or even gets worse!

    Scenario 1.

    No one likes cleaning the breakroom fridge but it has to be done. The last three times it was Lee's turn to clean the fridge, he just "happened" to be in meetings all day and you or someone else on the team ended up having to do it for him.

    a. Use the worksheet below to write down at least ten things you can do to ensure that the problem does not improve or might even get worse.

    b. Review the list of items on the worksheet and place a check mark beside each behavior that you currently engage in during similar conflicts. (*You will need to use your imagination for this!*)

Aiki Worksheet

✔		How can I ensure that the problem does not improve or even gets worse?
	1.	
	2.	
	3.	
	4.	
	5.	

✔		How can I ensure that the problem does not improve or even gets worse?
	6.	
	7.	
	8.	
	9.	
	10.	

c. Create a plan to counter these behaviors.

_____

_____

_____

_____

_____

d. Review your list again and look for new strategies that you could add to your plan.

_____

_____

_____

e. Summarize the steps you would take to resolve the conflict.

_____

_____

_____

_____

_____

Scenario 2.

You asked Kim for her report at the last project meeting. She said she would need to pass on providing any information. She explained that she didn't have the report completed and didn't want to give partial details until she had confirmed her conclusions. You then discovered she had turned in the final report to your supervisor less than an hour after the meeting. You are feeling like she deliberately withheld information to make you and your project look inept.

a. Use the worksheet below to write down at least ten things you can do to ensure that the problem does not improve or might even get worse.

b. Review the list of items on the worksheet and place a check mark beside each behavior that you currently engage in during similar conflicts. (*You will need to use your imagination for this!*)

Aiki Worksheet

✔		How can I ensure that the problem does not improve or even gets worse?
	1.	
	2.	
	3.	
	4.	
	5.	
	6.	
	7.	
	8.	
	9.	
	10.	

c. Create a plan to counter these behaviors.

_____

_____

_____

_____

_____

d. Review your list again and look for new strategies that you could add to your plan.

_____

_____

_____

e. Summarize the steps you would take to resolve the conflict.

_____

_____

_____

_____

_____

Scenario 3.

Peter is consistently 10-15 minutes late arriving in the morning and he often leaves 10-15 minutes early at the end of the day. His work is outstanding, so his work pattern isn't really an issue. The problem is that some of his team-mates have started working on Peter-time and team productivity is suffering.

a. Use the worksheet below to write down at least ten things you can do to ensure that the problem does not improve or might even get worse.

b. Review the list of items on the worksheet and place a check mark beside each behavior that you currently engage in during similar conflicts. (*You will need to use your imagination for this!*)

Aiki Worksheet

✔		How can I ensure that the problem does not improve or even gets worse?
	1.	
	2.	
	3.	
	4.	
	5.	
	6.	
	7.	
	8.	
	9.	
	10.	

c.   Create a plan to counter these behaviors.

_____

_____

_____

_____

_____

d. Review your list again and look for new strategies that you could add to your plan.

_____

_____

_____

e. Summarize the steps you would take to resolve the conflict.

_____

_____

_____

_____

_____

2. Applying the Aiki Breakthrough Change Model to your conflict.

a. Choose a conflict that you are dealing with now, you have dealt with in the past, or you expect to deal with in the near future.

Conflict: _____

_____

_____

b. Use the worksheet below to write down at least ten things you can do to ensure that the problem does not improve or might even get worse.

c. Review the list of items on the worksheet list and place a check mark beside each behavior that you are currently engaging in.

Aiki Worksheet

✔		How can I ensure that the problem does not improve or even gets worse?
	1.	
	2.	
	3.	
	4.	

✔		**How can I ensure that the problem does not improve or even gets worse?**
	5.	
	6.	
	7.	
	8.	
	9.	
	10.	

d. Create a plan to counter these behaviors.

_____

_____

_____

_____

e. Review your list again and look for new strategies that you could add to your plan.

_____

_____

_____

f. Summarize the steps you will take to resolve the conflict.

_____

_____

_____

_____

g. Execute your plan!

h. To increase your commitment to your plan, listen to the Aiki self-hypnosis recording at:

www.conflictatworkbook.com/resources.

Deeper Thoughts

Set a timer for five minutes. Choose one of the following questions and write down your answer as it relates to the plan you developed in the last exercise. Continue writing until the timer rings.

1. What new insights about the conflict did I gain after completing the Aiki brainstorm? In what ways, that I was previously unaware of, might I have been contributing to the conflict?
2. What might get in the way of executing my change plan? Are there steps I can take to minimize the probability of something getting in the way?
3. Do I need additional resources or someone's help to execute this plan? If so, how will I access these resources or recruit the help that I need?
4. After listening to the Aiki recording, how do I feel about executing my plan?
5. What other issues that I am dealing with could be resolved by applying the Aiki Breakthrough Change method? When will I do that? Are there others who could help me with the brainstorm process? If so, how will I involve them in the exercise?

My thoughts:

_____

_____

_____

_____

_____

_____

_____

_____

_____

_____

_____

_____

_____

CLEAN/N

Can we talk?

List the facts.

Explain your meaning.

Ask for their meaning.

Neutralize / Next Steps

Twelve
The CLEAN/N Model

Dealing with the really difficult conversations

Many difficult conversations can be resolved easily using any combination of the less direct tools discussed thus far. However, when a conflict has risen to the level of dispute or discord, a more structured conversation will be needed and this is what the CLEAN/N approach provides. If you integrate any of the other tools with the CLEAN/N approach, it will be even more effective in resolving the conflict.

The challenge for resolving a dispute or discord is that both sides have added multiple layers of interpretation to the facts of the situation. These interpretations are focused on the other party's intentions. Also, each party's Reticular Activating System guarantees that their interpretations will differ. More importantly, each side will see themselves as the victim and the other party as the villain.

> *In most conflicts, both sides are convinced they are the victim and they have very different interpretations of the facts. The CLEAN/N model guides both parties to a healthy dialogue.*

The CLEAN/N approach unravels these opposing interpretations. This guides both parties to a healthier dialogue which opens the door to a better result for both sides.

Can we talk?

The CLEAN/N approach begins by asking, "Can we talk?" This gives the other party some sense of control. There may be legitimate reasons for not holding the conversation "this minute" and asking permission to have the conversation demonstrates respect for the other party's priorities and context.

You should start creating and maintaining safety in this step and this should continue throughout the conversation. Safety tools consist of: showing that you care, apologizing if there has been a transgression, establishing a shared purpose, or using a contrast tool. These are all good tools for creating safety. They can be used individually or you can combine them for an even greater effect.

117

Apologizing is a familiar tool and does not require a lot of explanation. Showing that you care is also familiar but there is one aspect of it that is worth looking at more closely.

Saying something kind or clarifying your respect for the other person is a straight-forward strategy for showing that you care. However, we don't always think about listening as a tool for demonstrating caring - but being listened to is a gift we all crave. To help you to get past just hearing the other person to truly listening in a way that builds trust, I suggest using the acronym: CARE to listen.

C – Seek clarity by asking open-ended questions.
A – Assure the other person by verbalizing your positive feelings for them.
R – Rephrase key concerns that the other party may have shared.
E – Encourage the other party to continue sharing with filler words and nods.

Creating shared purpose and contrasting also require a little explanation.

It is hard to talk to someone when they are on the other side of a wall. When you establish a shared purpose, it puts you and the other party on the same side of the wall. It makes it clear that you are both working toward the same outcome, it's just your strategies that are different. A simple statement such as, "We both want this project to succeed" can remind both parties that they share the same goal.

Contrast statements are the most powerful tool for creating safety but they are not something you learned growing up. Developed by the authors of *Crucial Conversations*, this tool creates safety by clarifying your intention. In a discord or dispute, the other party sees you as the villain, someone who is intending to do them harm. The contrast statement begins with a clear statement that you are not intending harm and then it specifies exactly what your intention is. For example: "I don't want to control your personal style; what I do want is to be sure you understand the dress code."

Listing facts

The next step is to list the facts. Facts are objective and can be verified. Facts can be captured by a video camera - either you smiled or you didn't; you stood up or you stayed seated. By listing the facts, you create a base of agreement because they are devoid of differing interpretations.

Explaining your meaning

Once you have listed the facts, you can now share your own interpretation of those facts. What meaning did you draw from the sequence of facts? What are you feeling? Your interpretation of those facts is almost guaranteed to be different from the other party's interpretation. Because of this, it is not unusual for the other party to feel defensive when you share your meaning. If you detect defensiveness in either body language or verbal response, you will need to create safety by using one or more of the safety tools before continuing the discussion.

Asking for their meaning

Since the meaning you attached to the facts is most probably different from the other party's meaning, you must ask them to share their version of what the facts meant to them. This is not yet the time to problem-solve. If you try to solve the problem before the other party has had the opportunity to share their meaning, you will increase their resistance. They need the chance to share their perspective.

If you stay quiet and listen carefully to their story, one of two things will happen. The conflict might resolve itself because you now have information you were previously missing. The other outcome is that you now have a better understanding of the other person's perspective and they feel heard. You now have a better base to work from for problem-solving.

Neutralizing emotions

While listening to the other party's meaning, it is not unusual for you or the other person's defensive emotions to increase. Once again, if this happens, safety must be restored before proceeding to problem-solving.

Next steps

The final step is to create a plan. This is the problem-solving phase of the model. At this point, both sides have been heard and you have built a foundation of respect. From this base, a win-win result can be discovered.

Exercises

Applying the CLEAN/N model

Choose one of the following scenarios. Assume that you are Joyce, Kim or Leo and complete the CLEAN/N worksheet. You might need to add additional detail to the scenario to complete some portions of the worksheet.

Scenarios:

a. Brad and Joyce are each representing their own departments on an update of a policy that has major implications for both departments. Getting it rewritten is a high priority, given that there is a new regulation that will go into effect at the start of the next quarter. The parties agreed on a schedule of three two-hour meetings so that they could get this work done in enough time to comply with the new regulation.

   During the first meeting, Brad had an emergency at home and left after the first hour. Joyce summarized the work they had completed and tried to move forward without Brad. At the next meeting, Brad didn't like the work that Joyce did in his absence and insisted that they start from where they had left off at the last meeting. Joyce was annoyed but, in the interest of meeting the deadline, she didn't argue with Brad and they began working. Brad was interrupted by his staff three times during this second meeting and this slowed their progress. With only one meeting left and the deadline looming, Joyce was feeling rather anxious. When she arrived for the third meeting, Brad's administrative assistant informed he that Brad was running thirty minutes late.

b. Kim was meeting with several customers and she wanted to impress them. She scheduled the most comfortable conference room in the building and even booked the room for an extra half hour before the actual start of the meeting. This way she could ensure that the snacks and beverages she ordered would be properly set up before her guests arrived.

   When she got to the conference room 15 minutes before the meeting, she found her snacks and beverages on a cart outside of the room and another meeting in progress. Kim checked the posted schedule to confirm that she had indeed booked the room and then knocked on the door. Looking through the window beside the door, she could see the leader of the meeting wave her off. She knocked again and the leader, looking very annoyed, walked over to the door and informed Kim that the meeting was winding down and would be another 5-10 minutes. This was NOT the first time this particular colleague had disregarded the conference room schedule.

c. Leo's team was meeting to discuss a proposed project. After Leo made a suggestion for the project, his supervisor, Malik, reminded the team that they needed to be careful to honor the scope of the project. Leo didn't believe that his suggestion was outside of that scope and, careful to be respectful in his choice of words, said so. Malik, looking directly at Leo, said "Some members of this team don't understand the purpose of this project." Malik then turned away and asked the rest of the group for their input.

Malik and Leo had been colleagues and, even prior to Malik's promotion, Leo often felt that Malik would disagree with him in meetings just to disagree. Now that Malik was his supervisor, things felt even more personal. Leo wondered if Malik was deliberately singling him out in meetings and whether he should possibly be looking for another position.

CLEAN/N Worksheet

1. Can we talk?
    How will I ask permission to have the conversation about the conflict?

    _____

    Which safety tools will I use? [*Using more than one tool is always more effective.*]

    _____ Show that I care
    _____ Apology
    _____ Highlight a shared purpose
    _____ Contrast statements

    How will I show that I care?

    _____
    _____

    How might I use CARE (*Clarity, Assuring, Rephrasing and Encouraging*) to listen? Using CARE to listen is a good strategy for further demonstrating that you care.

    _____
    _____

If appropriate, how will I apologize?

_____

_____

What might be our shared purpose?

_____

_____

What contrast statements might I use?

1. _____

2. _____

3. _____

2. List your facts.
    [*Begin by brainstorming all the facts in the scenario and then place a check mark beside the facts that you will present in the conversation with the other party. There are always more facts than you will use but listing them all out will help you to identify the most important facts.*]

    ☐ _____

    ☐ _____

    ☐ _____

    ☐ _____

    ☐ _____

    ☐ _____

    ☐ _____

    ☐ _____

    ☐ _____

    ☐ _____

3. Explain your meaning.
    [*Describe what the facts mean to you. What conclusions have you drawn? What is your interpretation of the facts?*]

    _____

    _____

    _____

_____

_____

_____

4. Ask for the other party's meaning.
    [*How will you ask for their perspective or meaning? Make your ask simple and be careful to avoid problem-solving here.*]

    _____

    _____

5. Neutralize emotions.
    [*Sharing your meaning and hearing the other party's meaning often heightens emotions; you will usually need to be ready to reinstate safety at this point.*]
    Which safety tools will I use? [*Using more than one tool is always more effective.*]

    _____ Show that I care
    _____ Apology
    _____ Highlight a shared purpose
    _____ Contrast statements

    How will I show that I care?

    _____

    _____

    How might I use CARE (*Clarity, Assuring, Rephrasing and Encouraging*) to listen? Using CARE to listen is a good strategy for further demonstrating that you care.

    _____

    _____

    If appropriate, how will I apologize?

    _____

    _____

    _____

    What might be our shared purpose?

    _____

    _____

Next Steps:

What next steps might I propose?

[*Be careful to be open to other ideas that might surface later when you have the conversation. This is just some preliminary thinking.*]

_____

_____

_____

_____

_____

_____

Planning a real conversation with the CLEAN/N model

Choose a conflict that you are dealing with now, you have dealt with in the past, or you expect to deal with in the near future.

Conflict: _____

_____

_____

CLEAN/N Worksheet

1. Can we talk?

   How will I ask permission to have the conversation about the conflict?

   _____

   Which safety tools will I use? [*Using more than one tool is always more effective.*]

   _____ Show that I care

   _____ Apology

   _____ Highlight a shared purpose

   _____ Contrast statements

How will I show that I care?

_____

_____

How might I use CARE (*Clarity, Assuring, Rephrasing and Encouraging*) to listen? Using CARE to listen is a good strategy for further demonstrating that you care.

_____

_____

If appropriate, how will I apologize?

_____

_____

What might be our shared purpose?

_____

_____

What contrast statements might I use?

1. _____

2. _____

3. _____

2. List your facts.

   [*Begin by brainstorming all the facts in the scenario and then place a check mark beside the facts that you will present in the conversation with the other party. There are always more facts than you will use but listing them all out will help you to identify the most important facts.*]

   ☐ _____

   ☐ _____

   ☐ _____

   ☐ _____

   ☐ _____

   ☐ _____

   ☐ _____

☐ _____
☐ _____
☐ _____

3. Explain your meaning.
    [*Describe what the facts mean to you. What conclusions have you drawn? What is your interpretation of the facts?*]

    _____
    _____
    _____

4. Ask for the other party's meaning.
    [*How will you ask for their perspective or meaning? Make your ask simple and be careful to avoid problem-solving here.*]

    _____

5. Neutralize emotions
    [*Sharing your meaning and hearing the other party's meaning often heightens emotions; you will usually need to be ready to reinstate safety at this point.*] Which safety tools will I use? [*Using more than one tool is always more effective.*]

    _____ Show that I care
    _____ Apology
    _____ Highlight a shared purpose
    _____ Contrast statements

    How will I show that I care?

    _____
    _____

    How might I use CARE (*Clarity, Assuring, Rephrasing and Encouraging*) to listen? Using CARE to listen is a good strategy for further demonstrating that you care.

    _____
    _____
    _____

If appropriate, how will I apologize?

_____

_____

_____

What might be our shared purpose?

_____

_____

_____

Next Steps:
What next steps might I propose?
[*Be careful to be open to other ideas that might surface while you are having the conversation. This is just some preliminary thinking.*]

_____

_____

_____

_____

_____

_____

Note:

For future work, you can download a CLEAN/N Worksheet from
www.conflictatwork.com/resources

Deeper Thoughts

Set a timer for five minutes. Choose one of the following questions and write down your answer. Continue writing until the timer rings.

1. Why is it so difficult to let go of my meaning and to hear the other party's meaning?
2. What would be different in my life if I improved my ability to use the CLEAN/N model with difficult conversations?
3. Think about a specific conflict. What do I really want? If I continue to behave the way I have been and don't use a CLEAN/N approach, will I get what I really want?
4. Given a specific conflict, I have attached a meaning to the facts. What other meanings would fit the same set of facts? How do I feel about these alternative interpretations of what the facts mean?
5. How will I muster the courage to use the CLEAN/N model in a difficult conversation? Which of the many other tools for managing emotions might I use?

My thoughts:

_____

_____

_____

_____

_____

_____

_____

_____

_____

_____

_____

_____

_____

One size does NOT fit all!

Choose the right tool for the right situation.

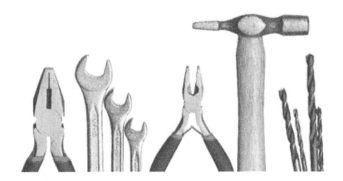

Thirteen
Using the Tools

Choosing

When you have too many choices, it can feel overwhelming. As a result you might delay your decision, or even not make one at all. The book, *Conflict at Work*, offers many tools for you to consider. The advantage of so many tools is that you can choose the ones that you feel most comfortable with and are the best match for resolving the issue you want to address. The downside of so many tools is the risk of indecision.

Matrix of Conflict Management Tools

To help narrow your choices while still ensuring that you are selecting the right tool for the situation, you can use the Matrix of Conflict Management Tools below. The matrix is structured on two axes:

- how much effort it takes to implement a tool, and
- who the change is focused on: yourself, others, or both.

> *Choose a tool that you are most comfortable using and best matches the issue to be resolved.*

Effort Expended

High

Self	Both	Others
Challenge Irrational Beliefs	Forgiveness	CLEAN/N Conversation
	Kindness	Scripting
	Aiki Change	Behavioral Conditioning Tools
		Extinction of Behavior
Mindset	De-Coding Language	Contrasting
Self-Talk		CARE to Listen
Affirmations	Body Language	STAND Up
		Principles of Influence
Self-Hypnosis	Triggers & Sparks	
Mindfulness	Language Patterns	Storytelling
Meditation		
Increase DOSE	Affirming Others	
Power Pose	Shared Purpose	Apology

Low

Self   Both   Others

Focus of Change

The tools:

All the tools are listed in the table below, with a short description and also where more information can be found in the companion book, *Conflict at Work*.

Tools	Brief Description	Effort	Focus	More detail
Power Pose	Posture that takes up maximum space. Delivers non-verbal message of confidence to self and others.	Low	Self	Ch. 7
Shared Purpose	Safety tool that breaks down separation of the two parties by bringing their shared goal to awareness.	Low	Both	Ch. 11
Apology	Safety tool that involves an admission of error with an expression of regret.	Low	Others	Ch. 11
Increase DOSE	Using specific behavior to increase your production of the feel-good neurotransmitters: Dopamine, Oxytocin, Serotonin, and Endorphins.	Low	Self	Ch. 4
Affirming Others *(Showing you care / Assuring)*	Safety tool that assures the other party that you care about them and/ or respect them.	Low	Both	Ch. 11
Self-Hypnosis Mindfulness Meditation	Creates the emotional space for a clearer perspective and accesses inner resources for more creative problem-solving.	Low	Self	Ch. 9
Triggers and Sparks Language Patterns	Words that provoke a predictable conditioned emotional response. Triggers produce a sense of threat and sparks generate energy and positive emotions.	Low	Both	Ch. 7
Storytelling	Communication tool for building empathy. It helps the other feel what you feel.	Low	Others	Ch. 7

Tools	Brief Description	Effort	Focus	More detail
Mindset Self-talk Self-Affirmations	Focusing your stream of thoughts on positive themes. Seeing behavior from a growth perspective and providing positive "I am..." statements that are true and relevant.	Medium	Self	Ch. 5
Body Language	The most basic and honest communication channel. It is the first language learned. Meaning is communicated through gestures, tonality, posture and body positioning.	Medium	Both	Ch. 7
Principles of Influence	Patterns of behavior that alter a person's focus. People change their behavior without being consciously aware how they have been influenced to do so.	Medium	Others	Ch. 9
STAND Up	A set of tools for dealing with a conflict when you have been blindsided. Stop; Take a breath; Actively listen; Neutralize emotions; Decide on next steps.	Medium	Others	Ch. 13
CARE to listen	A safety tool for understanding others' perspective. Clarity; Assure the other; Rephrase what you hear; Encourage the other party to continue sharing their perspective.	Medium	Others	Ch. 13
Decoding Language	The words we use to communicate do not always convey the same meaning to the other party. To remove confusion and increase understanding, the intended meaning of words needs to be clarified.	Medium	Others	Ch. 7
Contrasting	A tool for creating safety by identifying what is not your intention and then clarifying what your intention is.	Medium to High	Others	Ch. 11

Tools	Brief Description	Effort	Focus	More detail
Aiki Change	A brainstorming tool for getting unstuck by accessing your subconscious knowledge. The tool uses a paradoxical approach by asking how you can ensure that the conflict is not resolved and then reversing the answers to find new solutions.	High	Both	Ch. 10
Kindness	Demonstrating empathy and/or sympathy and engaging in actions that are helpful and/or supportive of the other party.	High	Others	Ch. 6
Behavior Conditioning	The consistent response to stimuli based on its pairing with other stimuli. The most common application is the use of rewards to increase a desired behavior.	High	Others	Ch. 8
Behavior Extinction	Reduction of a behavior through the withdrawal of the reward that has maintained the behavior.	High	Others	Ch. 8
Challenging Irrational Beliefs	The process of challenging those beliefs about how the world works that are causing misunderstanding and misery.	High	Self	Ch. 9
Forgiveness	The act of acknowledging hurts that others have inflicted and then releasing resentment and anger so that it does not continue to cause pain.	High	Both	Ch. 6
CLEAN/N Conversation	A sequence of steps for holding a difficult conversation. Can we talk; List the facts; Explain your meaning; Ask for their meaning; Neutralize Emotions / Next Steps.	High	Others	Ch. 11
Scripting	The practice of thinking through, on paper, each of the steps involved in the CLEAN/N conversation.	High	Othes	Ch. 11

Using the Matrix of Conflict Management Tools

To use this tool, you will need to ask yourself three questions:

1. Will the situation resolve itself?

    Some situations will resolve themselves with little or no effort. If this is the case, the tools at the lowest end of the effort continuum will be all you need. The advantage of using these tools, even though the situation will resolve itself, is that they serve to increase your optimism about your life and your future and they can strengthen a relationship.

    Although a situation might resolve itself with little or no intervention, don't get lulled into a false sense of security. If the same situation re-occurs several times, the pattern needs to be addressed with a tool that requires more effort. If the pattern is not addressed, you risk the situation moving up the conflict continuum to a more serious problem.

2. How stressed am I about the situation?

    The level of stress you feel when dealing with a conflict is an important indicator of how much energy you should invest in its resolution. Rate your stress on a 10-point scale. At 10 you would be completely immobilized, it's all you can think about. A stress level of 1 would mean that you are aware of the situation but it isn't interfering with your quality of life, your sense of safety, or your ability to function.

    If your stress level is somewhere between 1 and 3, then you can choose tools at the lower end of the effort continuum. If your stress level is between 4 and 7, you should focus your attention on the tools in the mid-range of the effort continuum. You might consider using more than one tool for added effectiveness.

    Finally, if your stress level is an 8 or higher, it's time to bring out the power tools. Focus your attention on the tools at the top end of the effort continuum and add additional tools from elsewhere in the matrix. With the stress level this high, chances are that you will need to use the CLEAN/N tool and if so, use the worksheet to help you plan your conversation. A CLEAN/N worksheet is available for download at:
    www.conflictatworkbook.com/resources.

3. Where on the conflict continuum does this situation fall?

Sometimes we are not good at evaluating our own level of stress. The stress signals might be subtle, or we are simply not attending to them. Another way to determine which tools you should focus on is to establish where on the Continuum of Conflict the situation is located.

If the situation is at Levels 1-3 - irritation, worry/troubled, or misunderstanding - then using the tools that need less effort would be an appropriate choice.

For situations that are at Levels 4 or 5 - disagreement and argument - you might choose to combine two or more tools from the low to mid-level range on the effort scale.

Finally, if the situation has risen to the top two levels, 6 and 7 - dispute and discord - you will want a comprehensive plan, using the tools that require a considerable investment of time and energy. At this level, it would be wise to use more than one tool and you might consider adding tools lower in the matrix for added effectiveness.

Dr. M. Paula Daoust

Exercises

1. For each of the following scenarios, select the tool(s) you would use. Explain your choice.

a. Gloria announced that she was going to retire in six weeks' time. Ever since her announcement, she has been abrupt and rude in her response to co-workers' questions. As her supervisor, you are annoyed by Gloria's behavior and concerned that it is affecting your team's performance. On the stressometer, you are at about a 3.

Conflict Level:	Tool(s):
Rationale for choice of tool(s):	

b. Last week you shared an idea with Randall. He presented the idea in today's meeting but didn't give you any credit for it. This isn't the first time he has done this to you or other members of the team. When you raised the issue with Randall after the meeting, he denied ever having had the conversation with you. You are feeling pretty steamed about it and you are probably at a 6 on the stressometer.

Conflict Level:	Tool(s):
Rationale for choice of tool(s):	

c. Your team has fallen behind on a critical project and, as the team leader, it will reflect poorly on you if you can't it get back on track. You can't move forward until Jeremy submits his report and he is more interested in working on his other projects. When you asked Jeremy when he would finish the report, he told you to get in line; he would get it done when he got it done. You tried to explain that the entire project was on hold until his report was done and he just got angrier. Your stress level is at an 8 on the stressometer.

Conflict Level:	Tool(s):
Rationale for choice of tool(s):	

2. Briefly describe a conflict situation that you are dealing with and answer the following questions.

Situation: _____

_____

_____

a. Is it likely to resolve itself without any action on your part?   Yes / No
    If yes, why do you think so?

    _____

    _____

    _____

How stressed do you feel about the situation?   _____

b. Where on the Continuum of Conflict does the situation lie?

    _____

c. Given your answers to the above questions, which tools would you use to resolve
    the situation? Your choice of tools should match the needs of the situation and
    how comfortable you feel with using them. Explain why you chose each specific
    tool.

Conflict Level:	Tool(s):
Rationale for choice of tool(s):	

Deeper Thoughts

Set a timer for five minutes. Choose one of the following questions and write down your answer. Continue writing until the timer rings.

1. Of all the tools in the matrix, which do I find the most difficult to use? Why?
2. Which of the tools in the matrix have I used most often? What result did I get when I used the tool? How might I use the tools most effectively?
3. Which of the tools in the matrix am I most interested in trying? In what situations will I use each tool and why?
4. Which of the tools in the matrix have I been applying to the wrong situations? What might the reasons be for doing this? What were the results of misapplying a tool?
5. Which of the tools in the matrix am I most interested in learning more about? Why? How will I go about learning more about that tool?

My thoughts:

_____

_____

_____

_____

_____

_____

_____

_____

_____

_____

_____

_____

_____

_____

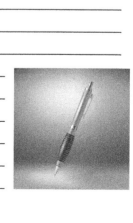

STAND
up to a
Blindside!

Fourteen
Blindsided

Assumption of the PPE model

The PPE model is:

> **P**reparing your emotions,
> **P**lanning your conversation, and
> **E**xecuting your plan.

This model assumes that you can anticipate when and where a conflict will happen. For most situations that involve conflict, you can choose when to deal with the issue. This allows you to prepare properly for an effective conversation.

Blindsided

Having the opportunity to prepare for a difficult conversation is ideal, but it is not always possible. Occasionally, you will be confronted with a situation that must be dealt with immediately. The situation is either urgent or the other party is highly emotional and confrontational. In either case, it is unlikely that you will be at your best.

Both your processing of the situation and your ability to problem solve will be sub-optimal. As a result, your response is unlikely to be as constructive as you would have wanted. When you are blindsided, you wade through the conversation as best you can. Later, you could work through a CLEAN/N worksheet to prepare for a better conversation with the other party. Once properly prepared, you can return and ask for a do-over.

> *When you are blindsided by a conflict, you will not be able to do your best thinking. The goal in these situations is to just minimize the damage.*

But what do you do to minimize damage in the middle of a conflict in which you were blindsided?

STAND up to conflict

The STAND up tool will help you to improve your response when you have been blindsided. When well executed, it will sometimes guide you to a resolution. More often, however, it will simply minimize the damage so that you can return later and deal with the situation effectively.

STAND is an acronym for a series of steps you can use to respond to a blindside:

Stop:
Wait for a minute or two before you respond.

Take a breath:
Get more oxygen into your system so that you can think more clearly.

Actively listen using CARE to listen.

Neutralize negative emotions.

Decide on next steps:
- o   When and where to have a deep discussion; or
- o   How to resolve the issue.

Exercises

1. Choose one of the following scenarios and answer the questions below.

   a. Drake slammed his notebook down on Rodney's desk, "Why did you take the travel laptop when you knew I was going to need it for my meeting today?"

   b. Daniel was explaining to the cross-divisional team, "We didn't make our numbers this month because production was slow in getting us the product and ..."
   Before he could finish his sentence, Carla who works in production interrupted, "You might get paid to sit around and make excuses, but in the meantime, we are working our butts off just trying to keep up with the orders we're getting!" she exclaimed.

   c. Ethan hesitated, "I agree that this needs to be done, but my team is already pressed to the limit."
   Matt answered angrily, "If you can't get this done, I'll find someone who can and you can start looking for other work."

   d. Missy couldn't take it anymore and she stormed into Kirk's office, "I can't believe you expect me to take on Alene's work. It just isn't fair," she cried out. "You are supposed to be the manager, but you aren't managing. You let Alene work at half-capacity and then you think I should pick up the extra work."

   e. Ivan finally caught up with Pat, "I sent you three emails and I left you two phone messages. You haven't responded to any of them. I need your answer and I'm tired of you just blowing me off!"

   After **stopping** and **taking a breath**, if you were Rodney/Daniel/Ethan/Kirk/Pat (circle one) you would:

   Actively listen:

   a. What questions might you ask to *clarify* the situation with Drake/Carla/Matt/Missy/Ivan?

   _____

   _____

   _____

b. How might you demonstrate that you care and/or *assure* Drake/Carla/Matt/ Missy/Ivan that you respect them?

_____

_____

_____

c. *Rephrase* Drake's/Carla's/Matt's/Missy's/Ivan's message to demonstrate that you understand what is upsetting them.

_____

_____

_____

d. What can you say to *encourage* Drake/Carla/Matt/Missy/Ivan to explain in more detail what they see as the problem.

_____

_____

_____

Neutralize emotions:

a. Which safety tool(s) would you recommend you choose:

_____ Show that I care
_____ Apology
_____ Highlight shared purpose
_____ Contrast statements

Explain the rationale for your choice:

_____

_____

_____

_____

_____

b. What should you do or say to apply your chosen tool:

_____

_____

_____

Decide on next steps:

a. If you want to delay this conversation to allow both parties to calm down, how should you ask for the delay?

_____

_____

_____

b. If there is an obvious solution to the problem, what might you suggest?

_____

_____

_____

_____

_____

_____

2. Consider a situation in which you were blindsided and answer the following questions.

Description of the situation:

_____

_____

_____

_____

_____

Actively listen:

a. What questions might you ask to *clarify* the situation with the other party?

_____

_____

_____

_____

_____

_____

b. How might you demonstrate that you care and/or *assure* the other party that you respect them?

_____

_____

_____

_____

_____

c. *Rephrase* the other party's message to demonstrate that you understand what is upsetting them.

_____

_____

_____

_____

_____

d. What can you say to *encourage* the other party to explain in more detail what he/they see as the problem.

_____

_____

_____

_____

_____

Neutralize emotions:

a. Which safety tool(s) would you recommend you choose:

_____ Show that I care
_____ Apology
_____ Highlight shared purpose
_____ Contrast statements

Explain the rationale for your choice:

_____

_____

_____

_____
_____
_____
_____
_____

b. What should you do or say to apply your chosen tool:

_____
_____
_____
_____
_____

Decide on next steps:

a. If you want to delay this conversation to allow both parties to calm down, how should you ask for the delay?

_____
_____
_____

b. If there is an obvious solution to the problem, what might you suggest?

_____
_____
_____
_____
_____

Deeper Thoughts

Set a timer for five minutes. Choose one of the following questions and write down your answer. Continue writing until the timer rings.

1. How frequently am I confronted with a conflict in which I am blindsided? How do I feel about the frequency? Is there something I might be doing to contribute to this frequency?
2. What makes it so difficult for me to be blindsided? Is there any specific situation in my past that makes being blindsided in conflicts especially difficult?
3. How does being blindsided in conflicts affect my willingness to address other conflicts?
4. How difficult is it for me to ask for a do-over after having been blindsided in a conflict?
5. Where in my life might am I most likely to be blindsided in a conflict? How will I prepare myself to use the STAND up tool more effectively?

My thoughts:

They are
NOT
the enemy!

Fifteen
Making It Work

Do something different

The definition of insanity is often described as doing the same thing and expecting a different result. When it comes to managing conflict, many of us are guilty of this insanity. We are using the same strategies we have always used. Either we join the White Knight club and avoid dealing with the situation with the hope that someone will rescue us or we join the other club, the Valiant Warriors, and we go on the attack.

Neither approach has worked well for us in the past and they are not working well for us now. It's time to do something different. You now have many tools to choose from. Be brave and experiment with better strategies until you find the ones that work well for you.

They are not the enemy

When a conflict is looming, it's easy to see the other party as the enemy. If only they would change their behavior, things would be so much better. The reality is, however, that they are not the source of your stress and anxiety. You are your own worst enemy. Your response to their behavior will either allow you to move forward to a better result or it will leave you stuck and stressed.

The tools described in this book are not worth the paper they are printed on if you don't learn how to use them. With practice, these tools can help you to respond to a conflict calmly and with confidence. Don't wait until you need the tools - the time to master them is now. Put in the work and I promise you, you will get the results you need and want while also strengthening important relationships.

Exercise Answers

Chapter 3: Levels of Conflict

1. For each of the following scenarios, decide which level on the conflict contin-
    uum it represents and explain why you think so.

    > **Levels of the Continuum of Conflict**
    > 1-Irritation; 2-Worried or Troubled; 3-Misunderstanding;
    > 4-Disagreement; 5-Argument; 6-Dispute; 7-Discord

    a. Your data is not reliable and I just can't agree to that strategy. My data indicates
        that we need to take this slower.

        Level: _5-Argument_
        You have a coherent set of reasons, statements or facts to support the position.

    b. I didn't want to come to this meeting. I have ten urgent emails I should be re-
        sponding to and instead, I'm sitting in this conference room waiting for George
        to get here so we can get started.

        Level: _1-Irritation_
        You are annoyed with the delay.

    c. I have done this a hundred times and I know what works. I am not about to settle
        for anything less because I know I'm right. Get on board or get out of my way.

        Level: _7-Discord_
        Zero-sum - it's your way or the highway. You must win.

    d. After I worked overtime to get the report done on time, Raoul was really critical
        of some of my conclusions. Now I'm not sure if I can work with Raoul. I'm just
        not sure of exactly what he wants.

        Level: _2-Worried/Troubled_
        You are anxious about the future and don't feel safe in your relationship with
        Raoul.

e. If we do it your way, we are going to polarize the team.

Level: __4-Disagreement__
You have a difference of opinion on appropriate action.

f. I sent a detailed email explaining my problem and asking for Brad's input. His response missed the point of my question. I don't think he gets what I'm trying to do and I wonder if he just doesn't want to be bothered.

Level: __3-Misunderstanding__
There is a breakdown in understanding.

g. I'm not going to stand for this. This is just not how we do business.

Level: __6-Dispute__
Winning is the focus, not understanding. You feel righteous about how business should be done.

Chapter 4: Dealing with Conflict: Common Approaches

1. Identifying facts.
    List the facts for each of the following scenarios. Be careful to list only things that could be verified.

    a. "Where is that report? I needed it an hour ago," Cal demanded.
        "I'm working on it, but the information Jill gave me doesn't balance. I need to check it out before I can finalize the report," Bob responded.

        Facts:
        Cal asked for a report. He needed the report an hour ago. Bob said he is working on the report. The information Jill sent isn't balancing. Bob is checking on the data before he will finalize the report.

    b. "We can get started as soon as everyone is here. Anyone know where Mandy is?" Angela asked.
        "Mandy is on Mandy-time. She's always ten minutes late. We can start without her, she'll be here soon," Richard answered.
        "No, this is too important. We need everyone's input. You can grab a cup of coffee while we wait," Angela insisted.

Facts:
Angela is waiting to start the meeting until everyone is present. Mandy is not present at the meeting. Richard suggested they start without her. The meeting is important. Angela wants everyone's input.

c. When Hayden got back to his desk, he found a note, "I thought we were meeting at 10. I'll check back with you later, Kate."
Hayden felt badly that he had missed Kate and immediately checked his calendar. He didn't see a meeting with Kate that he might have missed. He wondered what happened but remembered that this was not the first time Kate got her meeting schedule confused. He shrugged it off and began working on his latest project.

Facts:
There was a note on Hayden's desk. Kate thought they were meeting. Hayden didn't have a meeting scheduled on his calendar. Kate has gotten her calendar confused before. Hayden began working.

d. "The Chicago project has run into some snags. I need you to go out there tomorrow and see if you can fix it," Lance said.
Hannah wasn't happy with this news. She had promised to be at her daughter's recital the following night and traveling to Chicago would put that in jeopardy. Besides, Lance knew more about this project - he should be the one to go, not her. It wasn't fair that Lance was pushing this off on her!

Facts:
Lance wants Hannah to go to Chicago to fix the Chicago project. Hannah had promised to be at her daughters' recital. Traveling to Chicago would make attending the recital difficult. Lance knows more about the project.

e. The sign above the microwave clearly stated, "No popcorn." That didn't seem to matter to Diane, as she munched on popcorn during the meeting.

Facts:
There was a sign above the microwave that said "No popcorn." Diane was eating popcorn during the meeting.

2. Seeing multiple meanings.
For each of the scenarios in the previous exercise, provide at least three different meanings. At least one of the meanings should suggest a positive intention from the other party.
The answers below are suggested answers. Since the number of meanings for any set of facts can be extensive, you might have different answers from these. and that is fine. These answers will give you an idea of how the same facts can have different meanings.

a. The report:
Meanings:

1. Bob is using Jill as an excuse for not getting the report done on time.

2. The information is correct but Bob misread it.

3. Bob is highly conscientious about his work. You can depend on him to get it right.

d. The meeting:
Meanings:

1. Mandy is poorly organized and runs late often.

2. Mandy has no respect for other people's time.

3. Mandy is an important part of the team and has a lot on her plate so she sometimes runs late.

c. The note:
Meanings:

1. Hayden missed putting a meeting with Angela on his calendar.

2. Kate doesn't handle her caleandar well.

3. Hayden doesn't care about meeting with Angela.

d. Chicago:
Meanings:

1. Lance doesn't want to go to Chicago so he is sending Hannah instead.

2. Lance doesn't care about Hannah's person life.

3. Lance respects Hannah's expertise and knows she can do a good job on this project.

e. Popcorn:
Meanings:

1. Diane doesn't think the rule applies to her.

2. Diane didn't notice the popcorn sign.

3. Diane didn't use the microwave to pop her popcorn. She brought it from home already prepared.

Chapter 8: Decoding and Using Language Effectively

For each of the following scenarios, write down briefly what you could say and include at least three of the sparks described in the overview.

a.   You would like a team member to correct some errors on a report which they prepared for you.

b.   A colleague has asked you to cover the phones while they take a break. This is the third break they have taken this morning!

c.   You must introduce a change in a procedure and you expect that the change will be unpopular with your team.

d.   Your direct-report is ten minutes late getting to work. This has become a pattern.

e.   You need to assign someone to clean the break room refrigerator.

These are suggested answers only. You might have other equally valid answers.

	Sentence with at least three spark words
a.	Daphne, you probably already noticed the errors in the report. I was wondering if you have had a chance to correct them.
b.	Yes, if it's okay with Jan. I would be happy to do that for you because, Ray, I know you will do the same for me later today.
c.	You might want to look closely at this change because it will easily make our work less challenging.
d.	You probably already know what I need to talk with you about, Nate. I am wondering if, perhaps, there is something going on that is making getting to work on time an issue for you.
e.	Heather, I would really appreciate it if you would clean the break room refrigerator because you do such a great job. I understand that it isn't really your turn and you probably would prefer someone else do it but, in return, I can easily get Jean to cover your audit task which I know you hate doing.

Eliminating trigger words.

Re-write each of the following sentences by eliminating trigger words while maintaining the same meaning.

These are suggested answers only. You might have other equally valid answers.

a.   I was just going to get to it. You never give me a chance to get my work done.

Your project is next on my list, Peter. I recognize that you are looking for it now and I apologize that it isn't done already.

b. You should have taken more time when you entered the information in this report. It's all wrong and now I will have to correct it.

Becky, I'm wondering if you were rushed to get this report done. There are some errors in it that you don't normally make. I'll take some time now and correct them..

c. Why didn't you check the report before you submitted it? There are several avoidable errors in it.

To avoid errors, it is important to review reports before you submit them.

d. Don't take this personally but everybody is complaining that your cologne is giving them a headache.

You might not be aware but cologne can often cause headaches and there are some folks here who have complained.

e. Every day is the same thing. It's obvious that no one cares about this company as much as I do!

I care very much about this company and, based on some behavior, I'm not sure if others care as much as I do.

Chapter 9: Behavioral Science and Conflict

Applying the A-B-C sequence.

To help you see the application of antecedents, behaviors, and consequences, review the following scenarios and write down your answers to the questions.

a. Gerrard needed some additional office supplies. Instead of just walking down the hall and asking the supply clerk for what he needed, he chose to follow company procedure and fill out the appropriate forms. Surprisingly, when he submitted his request, it was rejected.

Antecedent	Behavior	Consequence (Circle one)
Gerrard needed office supplies.	*He filled out the appropriate forms.*	**Reward** **Punisher**

What do you predict Gerrard will do the next time he needs supplies?
Gerrard will not fill out the forms, he will simply walk down the hall and ask the clerk for what he needs.

If the organization wants employees to use the forms for requesting supplies, what might they do differently?
The organization will ensure that those who follow the correct procedure get their supplies and those who don't follow the rules do not get their supplies.

b. Helena stayed late to make sure that she could submit her report to Ray-Anne in time. The next day Ray-Anne told Helena that her work should have been completed during regular work hours and that she would not be paid overtime.

Antecedent	Behavior	Consequence (Circle one)
Helena had a report that needed to be completed.	*She stayed late to complete the report.*	**Reward** **Punisher**

What do you predict Helena will do the next time a report has to be submitted?
She will not stay late to complete the report.

If Rae-Anne wants Helena's best effort on future reports, how might she have handled this situation differently?
Rae-Anne should show Helena some appreciation by thanking her. She might also praise her for the effort and if possible, pay her overtime.

c. Arthur was having trouble closing a sale. A friend told him he was trying too hard and to listen more and talk less the next time he met with the customer. He tried this approach on his next visit and got the sale.

Antecedent	Behavior	Consequence (Circle one)
Arthur was on a sales call.	*He talked less and listened to his customer more.*	**Reward** **Punisher**

What do you predict Arthur will do the next time he meets with his customer?
Arther will focus on listening to his customer and talk less.

How might stimulus-generalization be applied to this situation to ensure continued success as a salesperson?

Arther will talk less and listen more to other customers.

d. Lilly was frustrated with the constant mess in the break room. She had complained about it in staff meetings several times but nothing improved. She decided to put a plan into place. Every time she went into the break room, she would find something that was clean and take a picture of it. She then posted the picture on the bulletin board with a simple "Thank you" post-it note attached.

Antecedent	Behavior	Consequence (Circle one)
Lilly wanted the break room to be kept clean.	*She posted a picture when she saw something clean with a message of "thank you."*	**Reward** **Punisher**

What impact do you predict Lilly's plan will have on the cleanliness of the break room?
People will start picking up after themselves and keeping the break room cleaner.

Why do you think Lilly's plan will have the effect you described?
People are being praised for cleaning.

e. Laird consistently arrived at meetings without the files he needed to participate fully. As a result, Erin, the team leader, often had to postpone the discussion of difficult decisions to the next meeting.

Antecedent	Behavior	Consequence (Circle one)
Laird doesn't have necessary files for the meeting.	*Difficult decisions are postponed.*	**Reward** **Punisher**

What impact is the postponement of discussions likely to have on Laird's future behavior?
Laird will continue to arrive at meetings without his files because difficult decisions are postponed.

What might Erin do if she wants to break the current pattern of behavior?
Go on with the meeting and complete the work, including making decisions, even if Laird does not have his files with him.

f. Micah was the leader of a project team that didn't work well together and members also did not like being questioned about their progress or decisions. Micah decided that he would follow every answer he got to his questions with a positive comment about some aspect of the answer.

Antecedent	Behavior	Consequence (Circle one)
Meetings with members who didn't like being questioned about their progress.	*Micah found something positive to say after each person spoke.*	**Reward** **Punisher**

What impact do you think Micah's positive comments will have on team members willingness to be questioned?
Team members will be more comfortable being asked about their work.

Why do you think so?
Instead of feeling threatened by possible criticism, their new experience is that they will be praised for something when they speak.

g. Jonas asked Alice for some information and was told that she didn't have it. A week later, it became evident that Alice did have the information and chose not to share it. Jonas contacted Alice's supervisor to complain about the lack of co-operation on Alice's part.

Antecedent	Behavior	Consequence (Circle one)
Alice didn't share information with Jonas.	*Jonas complained to Alice's supervisor.*	**Reward** **Punisher**

What impact, and for how long, do you think Jonas' complaint will have on the Alice's behavior?
In the future, Alice may give Jonas requested information but it might be incomplete. She will not be helpful to Jonas if she doesn't have to.

What else might Jonas have tried to improve Alice's willingness to share information?
Jonas might find an opportunity to be helpful to Alice so she will want to be helpful in return.

h. Things got a little tense in a meeting and Cynthia raised her voice and pointed her finger at a teammate. This was not the first time Cynthia engaged in this kind of behavior. Nate, her supervisor, told Cynthia to calm down and, in front of the team, reminded Cynthia that she was not being helpful.

Antecedent	Behavior	Consequence (Circle one)
Cynthia raised her voice and pointed her finger at a colleague.	*Nate told her to calm down.*	**Reward** **Punisher**

What impact would Nate's actions have on Cynthia's behavior and on their relationship?
Cynthia might resent Nate's actions.

Why do you think so?
Nate reprimanded her in public and she might feel embarassed.

i. Dana had to take some time off to care for a family member who was sick. As a result, her work fell behind and this was negatively affecting the team's productivity. Without saying a word to anyone, Emma quietly stepped in and started processing some of the files assigned to Dana.

Antecedent	Behavior	Consequence (Circle one)
Dana's work fell behind.	*Emma stepped in to help.*	**Reward** **Punisher**

What impact would Emma's behavior have on the team and on her relationship with Dana?
The team would work better and Dana would feel supported by Emma.

Why do you think so?
Dana would feel relief that the work was caught up and this relief is a type of reward.

j. Gina, the supervisor, was noticing that members of her team were leaving early. It would be different members on different days and it was usually not more than ten minutes early, but the lost work time was beginning to have an impact on the team's productivity. She decided that she would walk around the office at quitting time every day and exchange some small talk with each person who was still in the office.

Antecedent	Behavior	Consequence (Circle one)
Team members were leaving early.	*Gina walked around and chatted with people at closing time.*	**Reward** **Punisher**

What impact do you think Gina's evening tour would have on her team's behavior?
People would stop leaving early.

Why do you think so?
A friendly chat with Gina would be pleasant and, in addition, if they were not there, Gina would know.

Recommended Reading

Carson, Shawn and Tiers, Melissa (2014). *Keeping the Brain in Mind: Practical Neuroscience for Coaches, Therapists and Hypnosis Practitioners.* NY: Changing Mind.

Chabris, Christopher and Simon, Daniel (2011). *The Invisible Gorilla: How Our Intuitions Deceive Us.* Wexford, PA: Harmony.

Cialdini, Robert (2006). *Influence: The Psychology of Persuasion*, Revised Ed. NY: Harper Business.

Cuddy, Amy (2018). *Presence: Bringing Your Boldest Self to Your Biggest Challenges.* NY: Little, Brown, Spark.

Enright, Robert (2019). *Forgiveness is a Choice: A Step-by-Step for Resolving Anger and Restoring Hope.* Washington, DC: APA LifeTools.

Jonathan Haidt (2006). *The Happiness Hypothesis: Finding Modern Truth in Ancient Wisdom.* New York: Basic Books.

McGonical, Kelly (2013). T*he Willpower Instinct: How Self-Control Works, Why It Matters, and What You Can Do To Get More Of It.* Garden City, NY: Avery.

Medina, John (2014). *Brain Rules: 12 Principles for Surviving and Thriving at Work, Home and School,* 2nd Ed. Fall River, MA: Pear Press.

Patterson, Kerry, Grenny, Joseph, McMillan, Ron, and Switzler, Al (2011). *Crucial Conversations: Tools for Talking When Stakes Are High*, 2nd. Ed. NY: McGraw-Hill Education.

Schwartz, Barry (2016). *The Paradox of Choice.* NY: EccoPress.

Sullivan, Wendy and Rees, Judy (2008). *Clean Language: Revealing Metaphors and Opening Minds.* Williston, VT: Crown House Publishing).

Thomas, Kenneth W. and Kilmann, Ralph H.(1974). *Thomas-Kilmann Conflict Mode Instrument.* Tuxedo, NY: Xicom.

Other books by
Dr. M. Paula Daoust

Would you like get a reputation for getting difficult projects done on time, within budget, and with outstanding quality? Imagine how much more you could get done without corporate politics or if there was more collaboration and cooperation within your team and with other teams!

When you handle conflict well, you can get the results you need and want while strengthening important relationships. If you want to differentiate yourself from other managers, this is the book for you.

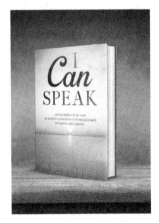

Whether it's a formal presentation, sharing ideas in a team meeting, talking with someone in authority a job interview, or giving a toast at a wedding, we all have to deal with a high-stakes speaking situation from time to time. It is a challenge to show up with our best self when we need it the most.

What difference would it make to your career if you could show up with your best performance when you need it the most? This book is chock full of practical, easy tools to get you there!

Would you like selling to be as natural as having a conversation with a friend?

We all sell, whether its products or services or proposing ideas, selling is an integral to all parts of business. When you put the science of emotional intelligence to work, selling becomes easy and success becomes automatic. This book will not only give you the tools, but it will help you understand why the tools are effective. Buy the book and start seeing the difference in both your career and your personal life!

Would your group or organization benefit from better conflict management skills?

Imagine what a difference better collaboration and co-operation would make in your work or group's environment! How much more would you and your folks be able to accomplish?

Dr. Daoust has delivered workshops to corporate and private groups for over twenty years. With expertise in instructional design, she can customize a workshop that is both engaging and capable of creating change in real time.

Depending on your needs, workshops can vary from two to eight hours. They can be delivered face-to-face or via Zoom. All workshops will include the book Conflict at Work and this companion workbook.

Dr. Daoust is also available for keynote presentations on a variety of subjects including conflict, speaking in high-stakes situations, emotional intelligence, work engagement and the scienc of sales.

For more information, contact
Dr. Daoust at:

DrPaula@behaviortransitions.com
785-633-6078

Made in the USA
Coppell, TX
16 August 2022

81589922R00098